MW00617262

AN ALTAR BOY GOES EAST:

DISCOVERING THE HEALING JESUS

Ted O'Brien

Disclaimer: The information contained in this book is for educational purposes only. Any medical condition discussed should only be cared for under the direction of a physician. Proper care from a physician should not be avoided, delayed or discarded when there is reason to consult a physician. This book is not designed to diagnose, treat or prescribe any disease. The author accepts no responsibility for such use. Conditions requiring proper medical attention should be referred to a physician.

Patient's names have been changed to protect their privacy.

DEDICATION

To my parents: You never raised a hand, never yelled and never lectured. You taught your children through leading by example and we thank you.

Thank you God for all your eternal blessings.

AN ALTAR BOY GOES EAST:
DISCOVERING THE HEALING JESUS

TABLE OF CONTENTS

ACKNOWLEDGMENTS:

To my friend and editor Mitch Maier: You worked tirelessly and never asked for a dime. Your efforts helped me transform this work and I am eternally grateful.

To my Facebook friends, for helping me chose a cover for this book.

Thank you!

Preface

The first time I laid my hands on someone to alleviate pain occurred when I was a child. Each summer my family and I piled into the station wagon and drove down to South Jersey to visit relatives. Our first stop was usually my dad's parents' house in Gloucester. While my parents, aunts and uncles, and grandparents gathered around the table to catch up over tall glasses of lemonade, my older sisters, cousins, and I played in the huge three-story house, running up and down the stairs, releasing pent-up energy from sitting for five hours in the car.

After we tuckered ourselves out, we joined the rest of the family for lemonade among the old-fashioned furniture, lava lamps, and relics. Then my grandmother told a family story. A tall, hunched woman with soft wrinkled cheeks in her eighties, she still cooked, kept house, and fought with fervor against any speck of dirt that dared to invade her home.

Usually, she spoke with passion and enthusiasm, but this time she kept reaching for her back and her face looked pained.

My dad leaned forward in his armchair. 'What's wrong, Mom?' he asked.

'I've got a bit of arthritis in my spine,' my grandmother replied through half-gritted teeth. 'I'll be fine.'

I didn't know much about arthritis back then and was curious. 'What's arthritis, Grandmom? Why does it hurt? Is there anything you can do to make it feel better?'

'Sometimes it helps if someone rubs my back,' she remarked.

I had trouble understanding why she had to suffer and wanted to help her feel better, so I responded, 'I can help, Grandmom.'

She led me into the living room, where we sat on her favorite couch. She faced away from me and I was left staring at the back of her utilitarian dress. I placed my hands on her and began to gently feel around. Not knowing a thing about massage or acupressure, I simply relied on her feedback and my instincts. I could feel the bony protrusions along her spine through her dress as I slowly navigated my way through the tender spots in her back. She had a pronounced slumping curvature in the middle of her back that didn't appear normal. I felt areas near her spine that were knotted and tight as if straining to support her weakened spine, yet other areas of her back felt soft and squishy. I began to get the hang of it as I moved my small hands up towards her neck and shoulders.

'That feels good,' my grandmother said with a smile in her voice.

It made me happy to ease her pain that day.

After I massaged her back, she perked up and regained her normal zest for storytelling. She shared with me a story of how she witnessed the Blessed Virgin Mary on the door of St. Mary's Church, which was just three doors down from her house on Monmouth St. in Gloucester, New Jersey.

Apparently, hundreds of people had witnessed the Blessed Virgin Mary on the church door over a period of a couple years during World War II. My dad even chimed in and mentioned how he saw the Blessed Virgin Mary on the door while he was walking home one night by himself when he was a kid. Sometimes the Blessed Virgin Mary would appear to single visitors and sometimes she drew large crowds at the church. People would wave things in front of the ghostly figure to see if it was a projection of some sorts. However, no one ever found out how the image appeared.

Even as a kid I had a deep faith in spirit. I knew this heavenly image was truly the Blessed Virgin Mary and never questioned it. In fact, I was perplexed hearing my dad talk about it in the car on the way back to Massachusetts. His science-based mind was trying to figure out some material explanation for the image. I argued, 'Dad, did you ever think that it may have actually been the Virgin Mary?'

He just shrugged and didn't have an answer.

From a young age, I was a devout Catholic who went to church every week and said my prayers every night before bed. At the age of ten I began an eight-year stint as an altar boy at St. Catherine's Church in my small hometown of Leeds, Massachusetts. I was quiet and shy as a youth but otherwise like most other kids. I loved to play sports and run through the woods with my friends after school. However, I possessed an unusual passion for spiritual matters, which I noticed was different from most other kids my age. I wanted to know more about the 'big' questions of life. Who were we, where did we come from, and where did we go after death? I had an innate faith in God and Jesus and was a committed Catholic. At the same, I always exhibited a curiosity about God and questioned things that didn't make sense to me.

I was especially inspired by the more mystical aspects of religion, such as visits from angels and the miraculous healing ability of Jesus Christ. I vividly remember the day my great-grandfather on my mom's side died when I was eight. An incredible story accompanied his death.

Very late in his life, my great-grandfather saw an angel at the foot of his bed. He discussed the encounter with the rest of the family the following night at dinner. He told my aunts, uncles, and grandparents that the angel informed him that he would pass the next night.

Sure enough, he passed away the next night. Only when it came true was this heavenly visit taken more seriously. To this day I still love hearing this story from my family as it fuels my faith in the afterworld.

However, my thirst for knowledge about the mystical aspects of Jesus' life was never fully quenched during my youth. I recall asking my parents, my Sunday school teachers, and even my priest, Father Vincent O'Connor, how Jesus performed his miracles. I wanted to learn more about his healing ministry, but I always received the same answer.

'Jesus' healings were miraculous acts of God. They're not to be understood further or replicated.'

Jesus suffered and died on the cross for all mankind, a selfless feat of enormous magnitude. I wondered as a child, however, how enriching it would be to see a living Jesus when you walk into church, rather than a lifeless Jesus hanging on the cross. Instead of paintings and statues of Jesus being murdered along the walls, how inspiring it would be to see more depictions of Jesus healing a blind man or raising someone from the dead.

Years went by before I eventually began a long and passionate education, seeking every bit of knowledge that I could about how to heal the human body. I've spent my entire adult life healing: healing myself of the ailments that plagued me for two decades beginning after college, healing my friends and family of various maladies, and healing thousands of patients in my private practice. The entirety of my healing practice has been through holistic and natural methods, particularly by the laying on of hands and using my energy, intention, and faith to promote healing within my patients. I now teach students how to awaken and cultivate their own God-given abilities to heal themselves and others. I feel very fortunate to pass on this knowledge my teachers have given me, so that many more can help eliminate the pain and suffering of those in need.

I believe that God came down from heaven two thousand years ago to show us how *he* could be like us by taking human form. He walked with us, laughed with us, and shared in our misery and pain. But furthermore, Jesus also came to show us that *we* could be like him. He continually told us that the kingdom of God is within us and assured us that others would perform the same miracles as he did. Imagine a world where we all evolved to his level of consciousness. This might be the 'heaven on earth' Jesus spoke of many times in the Bible.

Jesus told us repeatedly that we have the same miraculous abilities to heal. He told us we have Godly power within each one of us. Jesus encouraged us to 'move mountains' (Matthew 17:20), that 'all things are possible' (Matthew 19:26), and the kingdom of heaven is within us (Luke 17:21). However, the Bible lacks specific instructions how to replicate his feats. I've written this book to unveil evidence of this healing knowledge, and to show that we all have the power and ability to display it.

I've explored countless methods for healing the body and have studied some of the deepest and most esoteric forms of Eastern healing techniques. I've traveled to China and India and studied with Daoist monks and Hindu yogis, learning about qigong, yoga, and meditation.

I've applied these techniques toward my own healing pursuits and with thousands of my patients. This book, however, is not just about my physical travels East. It details what I've learned from many Eastern medicine teachers along the healing journey and how it helped me develop a greater relationship with my Lord Jesus Christ. Essentially, by learning how Eastern Masters performed their healings, I gained a new perspective into how Jesus Christ may have achieved his mastery of the healing domain.

On the surface, it may seem preposterous to associate Jesus with other religions, particularly Eastern religions. However, there is a much stronger link between Eastern faiths and Christianity than one might think, and I will share evidence of these many bonds. For me, learning about the specific practices one must go through to attain healing mastery in the East expelled much of the ambiguity about Jesus' healing abilities. It also provided actual tools, which inspired me to live out Jesus' assertion that we too can perform miracles.

My early Christian teachers were correct about Jesus' healing miracles. They *were* miraculous and they *did* come from God. However, I have come to believe that they were to be understood and emulated.

Chapter One:
The Initiation

Childhood Theft

When I was about five or six years old, I went to church with my family every Sunday morning. I can vividly remember sitting in the pew, watching the happenings with a curious eye. At first I didn't know much about Jesus or Catholicism, but from a young age I had a deep instinctive faith in a higher power and the concept of a heavenly place that one goes to when they pass from this earthly realm.

During mass one Sunday, I asked my mom if Father O'Connor was God. She smiled and explained to me that he was not God. He was simply the priest. I then asked her who Jesus was, and she pointed to one of the statues of Christ up on the altar. She told me how Jesus was

Ask, and it will be given to you;
seek, and you shall find;
knock, and it will be opened to you.

Matthew 7:7

the Son of God and came down to earth to teach and inspire us. This was my first introduction to Jesus Christ and God.

Months later, while sitting in the living room with my mother, I asked what I had to do in order to make it into heaven. My mother had been raised in a family steeped in Catholic faith and spent many years in Catholic school during her youth, so she knew the rules and teachings like the back of her hand. She taught me a bit more about Jesus, God, heaven, and the Catholic Church, but she also told me that there was a specific set of rules called the Ten Commandments. She explained that if I were to follow these laws that came from God, then I would most assuredly make it into heaven.

I was excited to have instructions to make it into heaven, and eager to follow them. While I familiarized myself with the Ten Commandments, I quickly realized that they mostly focused on what *not to do* rather than what *to do*.

A year later I started Sunday school. There I learned that there was not only a place called heaven that good people go to, but there was also a place called hell which was not such a happy place. I learned that if you didn't follow the Ten Commandments then you might be sent to hell to burn for an eternity! The concept of burning in hell scared me. I simply had to follow the Commandments.

I understood that I was not to covet, lie, steal, curse, murder, have sex with my neighbor's wife, or disobey my parents. This was my first introduction to the concepts of sex and murder. I was also taught that I must go to church on Sunday and love God with all my heart and soul. I took these rules very seriously. However, my initial inspiration to make it into heaven slowly turned into a terrified resolve to avoid hell.

Some months later, I snooped around in my sisters' room while they were at school. I came upon a small purple bottle with a cork plug at the top. I pulled the cork, sniffed inside, and discovered perfume for the first time. The sweet, flowery smell was amazing! I lifted the bottle to my nose for a few more sniffs. Suddenly I longed to take the pretty glass bottle with the precious scent without telling anyone. Immediately, a silent voice came into my head reminding me about the Seventh Commandment: 'Thou Shalt not Steal'—but the urge of desire won. I stole the perfume.

To this day I have no idea why I did. The potential consequence—going to hell—weighed on my mind, but I took the bottle anyway. It was as if something inside me wanted to challenge God's commands.

For weeks, I couldn't stop thinking about the torments I might have to endure in hell at the end of my life. Guilt, shame, fear, and unworthiness weighed on my mind.

I put the bottle back in my sisters' room where I found it. Would God forgive me?

I sought my mom's advice again, to find out how to obtain God's forgiveness. She told me about confession, where you could go to church and speak one-on-one with a priest about the sins you had committed. He could then grant clemency and wipe your slate clean. I was so glad that God had a process in which your sins could be absolved! Some of my fear and pressure to live up to the commands was lifted off my shoulders—such relief!

About a year later, I attended my first confession with my dad. I asked him many questions and he explained what I had to do. First, when my turn came up, I had to walk into the sacristy where Father O'Connor was sitting behind a closed door. I thought I understood.

When I walked into the empty silence of the sacristy, I was scared. The wood-paneled confessional loomed like a menacing closet. My only consolation was that Father O'Connor would not be able to see me, and might not know who I was.

With a fear-squeaky voice, I began to speak.

Then I heard Father O'Connor's soft, gentle voice. Was he telling me I had to go somewhere else? Confused and anxious, I froze.

The door creaked open.

Father O'Connor pointed to the confessional's other door, where I was supposed to enter. The secret of my identity was blown.

I stuttered my opening prayer and the ritual words of how

sorry I was to have committed sins. Then I told him this was my first confession.

Now was the time to confess first my mortal sins, then the venial ones. After my previous blunder, I was desperate to get this part right, but I was only seven and hadn't yet murdered anyone, committed adultery, stolen, worshipped false Gods, or cursed. I confessed that I had disobeyed my mother and father, even though I couldn't remember if I really had. So I was lying in the confessional. I also admitted to stealing my sister's perfume, but made sure to mention that I put it back.

Father O'Connor helped me finish with a prayer called the Act of Contrition: 'Oh my God, I am heartily sorry for having offended You. I detest all my sins because I dread the loss of heaven and the pains of hell. But most of all because they offend You, my God, Who are all good and deserving of all my love. I firmly resolve, with the help of Your grace, to sin no more and to avoid the near occasions of sin. Amen.'

Initial Preparation

As my commitment and involvement in the church grew, I became enthralled with being an altar boy. I watched in admiration as the older boys walked down the aisles during mass with their elegant capes and white robes. The processional candles they held as they approached the altar further magnified the important relics they carried.

So at the ripe age of ten, I eagerly began my training to become an altar boy for St. Catherine's Church. Father Vincent O'Connor introduced me to a senior altar boy, John Helms, to mentor and train me.

John first taught me the importance of genuflecting on one knee while crossing the middle of the altar, in front of Jesus and the Blessed Sacrament. This is done as a sign of reverence to honor Jesus Christ in the Holy Eucharist.

I then learned the entire process of the mass and what tasks each altar boy was to complete before, during, and after each service. First and foremost we entered the sacristy, the same room where I was introduced to confession at age seven. The sacristy is a small room for the priest and altar boys to prepare for each service. Various sacred items were stored there in a safe, and separate wardrobes contained vestments to be worn during mass for the altar boys and the priest. The general public is normally not allowed in this area at any time except for small weekday masses and occasional confessional usage.

John showed me where the sacred chalices were stored and I was given the code to the safe. Then I learned how to light the candles on the altar, prepare the water and wine, and arrange the furniture on the platform where priests and servers sat and kneeled. It was illuminating for me to learn more about the specific meaning behind each part of the service and the responsibilities that we undertook. For example, the water and wine represented the blood and fluids that poured from Jesus while on the cross. The Sanctus bells are rung three times, at special occasions during the mass. The first ringing is executed when the priest calls down the Holy Spirit over the bread and wine. The second is when the priest holds up the Holy Eucharist (bread) up in the air, just after the words, 'This is my body which will be given up for you.' The last time is after he lifts up the chalice, representing the blood of Christ. 'This is the cup of my blood, it will be shed for you and for all so that sins may be forgiven. Do this is memory of me.'

The first time I set foot on the sanctuary during a service, I nervously looked out into the pews, scanning for a sign of my mother. When I saw my parents, they smiled and seemed very proud. Suddenly, I felt honored to be assisting Father O'Connor and esteemed to be a significant part of celebrating the life of Jesus every Sunday. In a way I felt as if I was a step closer to Jesus and to God. I remember looking up and seeing the larger-than-life statue of Jesus on the crucifix up close and personal. It was an awe-inspiring sight.

After the service, we returned the altar back to its pre-mass state, putting out the candles, putting away the sacred items, and disrobing from our capes and cassocks. I enjoyed being an altar boy because it made me feel like I was a special part of the mass. Honestly,

I found it much more exciting than sitting in the church pews each week. Being an active part of the service kept me busy and made the Sunday mass more enjoyable. Despite the extra time and commitment that came with being an altar boy, it was worth it as the lengthy services went by much faster. Plus, Father O'Connor always showed his respect for his altar servers by taking us on field trips throughout the year. These included visits to the beach, to the bowling alley, to the movies, and to his lake house at Pine Island Lake in the hills of Westhampton, Massachusetts. Mostly, however, being able to serve as an altar boy somehow felt like working for Jesus and assisting God directly, which made me feel valued and important.

However, becoming an altar boy and learning all the rules and regulations of the church steeped me further into the dogma of sin. I felt daunted at times and did not want to let down Father O'Connor, but even more I didn't want to offend God. I developed a heightened sense of wrongdoing from learning the Ten Commandments and the many rules of the Catholic Church. Going to confession only reinforced this state of mind because I would try to identify my sins and seek forgiveness in order to avoid punishment. This pattern of sin, punishment, and forgiveness shaped my future actions because I greatly feared to make any mistakes.

Sorry Syndrome

This bred what I call the 'Sorry Syndrome.' I always apologized for my actions. I said sorry to my parents for minor infractions, apologized to my friends for trivial behaviors, and pled for my teachers' forgiveness when I felt I had done something wrong. I even dropped the 'S-bomb' while playing sports. I apologized to my teammates for missing a shot, to my coach for making a bad pass or turnover, and even to my opponents if I hit them too hard in contact sporting events like basketball, football or soccer. I was hard on myself. I wasn't perfect, but felt I had to be perfect in order to be accepted and to be a success.

Although the word 'sorry' became cemented into my vocabulary, I wasn't aware of it, because nobody ever called me out on it. This changed only many years later, when I was twenty-seven and had just completed my schooling in acupressure and had begun my practice of Chinese medicine. My teacher, Sam McClellan, referred a patient to me in the DC Metro area who had been suffering from back pain and sciatica for several months. I was excited to have one of my first professional patients.

About eighty years old, this woman came to my house for the treatments with her husband. She was cordial with a tough streak and unafraid to speak her mind. On the way up the sidewalk to my front door, she often snapped at her husband about every little thing.

I always welcomed her into the house, then took her to the spare bedroom on the first floor where I had my massage table set up. I began the treatment by having her lie on the table face down and performed acupressure and bodywork on her back and legs. As I progressed, I slowly palpated the areas of pain, and every so often she let out a slight 'Oww!' as I connected with the acupressure points with my fingers.

Quite naturally, I said, 'Sorry' each time I heard her 'Ouch!'

One day, I was pressing against a classically tender area in the hip on the piriformis muscle and she yelped a more audible, 'Owwww!'

I quickly chirped, 'Sorry!'

She pushed herself up off of the table, glaring at me as she growled in a deliberate tone, 'Don't say you're sorry!'

Then she lay back down on the table as if nothing had happened.

I was shocked. Why had my apology upset her? To me, the word 'sorry' was ranked right up there with 'thank you' and 'please.' How could I finish the treatment without using the word again?

I almost said 'sorry' for saying 'sorry' and just managed to swallow the word that was already on my tongue.

I finished her treatment without saying much at all.

For some time I pondered her reaction to my incessant apologizing. I realized that I was using the word 'sorry' often, but why was she getting so upset about it?

Then it hit me. If I had hired someone to do something that was important to me, I wouldn't want them apologizing to me constantly as they performed their work, implying sorrow and distress. I imagined myself lying on the operating table and hearing my surgeon say, 'Whoops! I am so sorry!'

Now I was getting it. My patient didn't want to pay money on an acupressure session from someone who was feeling distressed, upset, downcast, downhearted, or sad. I too would want a therapist who was happy, confident, positive, and energetic. God probably didn't want me feeling sorry about myself or for my actions either.

This insight reminded me of something I learned as a kid after a Little League game in which I had gone two for five with two strikeouts. My dad, seeing me dejected, sat me down and told me not to worry about it.

'Ted, guess what they do to hitters in the big leagues that fail sixty percent of the time?' He smiled. 'They send them to the Hall of Fame.'

I brightened up as I recalled Ted Williams—my namesake and my dad's favorite player—who was the last hitter to bat .400 in a season and the best hitter of all time.

I was then able to think about how to improve for the next game.

After that experience with my patient, I tried to lessen my use of 'sorry,' although I still felt a bit of guilt every time I made a mistake and didn't apologize.

'Mr. Needs'

Since I had grown up with this heightened awareness of my mistakes, apologizing became a part of my life. This pattern of thinking created a perfectionist outlook, which sometimes led to positive outcomes and prevented me from being complacent. However, it also bred a very low self-esteem as I became increasingly critical of myself.

At some point in my early years this self-critical behavior must have become too overwhelming because I slowly began projecting it onto others. As my ability to notice my own mistakes amplified, I grew more aware of other people's faults. I became self-righteous, opinionated, and critical of friends and loved ones. The 'Sorry Syndrome' now had a friend, and his name was 'Mr. Needs.'

I told people what they needed: 'Hey, let me help you with that, you're doing it wrong,' or 'Wait, you need to do it this way,' or 'No, no, no, let me show you how to do this.'

Although I thought I was helping, and usually offered my advice in a kind manner, my friends grew irritated. I couldn't understand why they were distancing themselves from me.

It took years before another of those 'Aha!' moments threw light on the issue.

In the summer of 2003 I was thirty-three years old and just beginning to reap the benefits of my growing acupuncture practice. Finally out of debt and with some free time on my hands, I decided to rekindle my passion for camping and purchased a good tent, camp cookware, a stove, and a sleeping bag. I made many trips to the majestic, lush Shenandoah National Park in the western portion of Virginia, sometimes alone, sometimes with friends. It was the perfect weekend getaway from the busy city life in the DC Metro area and helped me recharge my batteries.

During one of those visits I brought my friend Dave with me.

Dave hadn't been camping in years. From the way he tried to make a fire, scattering the sticks horizontally instead of in an upright pyramid, I could tell he was rusty at setting up a campsite. So, I happily took it upon myself to show him the ropes.

'Here, let me show you how to put the tent together,' and 'Dave, can you get a bucket of water from the river for me, please?' and 'Oh, no, you need to build the fire pit this way,' and 'You need to keep your food secure so we don't attract the bears.'

Although my intentions were good, there was one problem: Dave never asked me for any help. True, he was less experienced than I with camping, but he had done it before and wanted the freedom to do things in his own time and his own way. After half an hour of my unasked instructions, Dave snapped. 'I can do it myself, thank you!'

I thought he was unreasonably touchy. After all, I was just trying to help.

Later that night I sat down by the river to meditate, then went back to camp and went to bed. I stayed awake under the stars contemplating Dave's irritation with me. In years past I had written off my friends' irritation with me as *their* issues. But it happened so often, and I didn't want to keep losing friends.

As I lay under the stars, I realized what aspect of my behavior had been so abrasive. First, who was I to tell anyone else how they're supposed to do something? What right did I have to tell someone what I thought they needed to do? Telling a person that they need to do something disempowers them and takes their freedom of choice away.

I also realized that when you tell someone they *need* to do something it implies that there is a consequence to the matter at hand, which there isn't. By simply using the word need I am taking away their God-given gift of free will.

I, of all people, should understand this freedom, because I hate it when people try to tell me what *they* think that *I* need.

If I tell someone what I think that they need, it implies that there is only one way, my way! That was me, Mr. Self-Righteous, Mr. Arrogant, Mr. Needs.

Glass Half Empty

I always noticed what I was doing wrong, what others were doing wrong, and mostly just seeing what was wrong with life around me.

I prided myself in having the answer to everyone's issues, but those were only what I viewed as issues. This self-righteous perfectionist mentality made me unhappy and created unhealthy thought patterns in my mind.

What a depressing way to live life, always seeing the glass half empty instead of *completely* full! The real issue was my inability to see the self-righteous side of my behavior.

It was much easier to find imperfections in others than to admit my own arrogance and holier-than-thou attitude. Who was I to judge other people, and how did I become this way? More importantly, how could I cure this sanctimonious behavior?

My early introduction to the concepts of sin, wrongdoing, and punishment had bred negative thought patterns, encouraging the feelings of fear, guilt, shame, and low self-esteem. The focus on wrongdoing led me to see mistakes in myself and in those around me. I noticed inadequacies and diagnosed them, especially in other people.

I found that being taught to do good unto others by being commanded what *not to do* to others became a hindrance to my spiritual evolution. Although sinning is never a good thing, focusing on it too much was not helpful either.

I'm certainly not blaming my negative, self-righteous thought patterns solely on the Ten Commandments or on my early Christian training. Although we are molded by the world around us, and what we learn at an early age affects us deeply, not everyone who abides by those laws develops such a critical attitude to others. I accept the responsibility for my own thoughts. So it was solely my responsibility to change my attitude to a more understanding one.

Chapter Two:
My First Patient

My interest in healing grew throughout high school. Being a competitive athlete, I was always striving for an edge. My anatomy teacher, Mrs. Lauer, enlightened me about nutritional techniques to enhance performance for long distance runners. I learned about nutritional supplements and dietary regimes, like carbohydrate loading before cross-country races. This inspired me to major in Human Nutrition at the University of Massachusetts. But it wasn't until after college that my two passions of healing and spirituality slowly started to intersect.

After I graduated, I felt such a relief from the stresses of school. Minus the gut-wrenching final exams and oral presentations, my anxiety dissipated and I enjoyed an increased vitality and well being.

Beloved, I pray that all may go well with you and that you may be in good health, as it goes well with your soul.

Matthew 7:7

My appetite soon picked up and I finally began putting weight onto my naturally rail-thin body. The added weight delighted me and I pushed it further. My daily routine opened with a stop at Abdows Big Boy restaurant for their buffet breakfast on my way to work in Springfield, Massachusetts, ironically as a nutritionist. When lunchtime came, I got in the car, drove to the Chinese buffet, and stuffed myself to the gills with greasy entrees and rich deserts. For dinner I would come home and prepare simple, fast food friendly meals like Hamburger Helper or TV dinners. Then before bed I usually threw down a large dairy-based weight gain protein shake for even more calories.

Months later, after a considerable gain in weight, I was feeling listless and achy. My digestion became sluggish and I slowly started losing the weight I had put on. I wore all sorts of braces on my body when I played basketball to ease my joint pain, and my focus and concentration decreased at work to the point that I would even fall asleep at my desk. So I visited a few doctors to figure out what was wrong with my body.

After the doctors brushed me off as healthy without any blood work or tests, I took matters into my own hands. My girlfriend at the time inspired me to eat more salads, vegetables, and home-cooked meals. She also told me about an acupressure therapist who was helping her mother and thought that I might be interested in speaking with her.

Fascinated, I called the woman, and after speaking to her for a half hour I contacted the school she attended for acupressure training. Amazingly, the New England Institute of Integrative Acupressure was just five minutes away. Mind you, there was nothing in Leeds that was five minutes from my home except a post office, an elementary school, and a church. I lived in the boonies, so this was a pleasant surprise.

After speaking to one of the teachers, I signed up to take the classes, which conveniently began just two weeks later. By the second day, after learning some basic acupressure techniques, I was eager to find volunteers to practice on.

To my pleasant surprise, my father allowed me an attempt. Just two weeks before, he had urged me not to waste time with this class. He had scowled at the notion that I was spending half of my life's savings, about $2,000 at the time, on a Chinese medicine course he felt had no credibility whatsoever. 'Ted, don't waste your money on that stuff! There's nothing in the Brassworks building that can be worth spending a thousand dollars on.'

The Brassworks was the name of an old mill building, which had been converted into spacious office suites and shops near my home.

So there I was, zealously wanting to try and take away someone's pain and suffering. Yet my biggest critic and doubter was also my very first patient. Immediately, I was putting my limited skills and my father's skepticism to the test. So, as my dad lay on his favorite recliner in the living room, I sat there with my foot reflexology chart on the ottoman, ready to work on the ailing shoulder that had been bothering him for several months.

My dad cautiously watched as I started rubbing his feet. Since he had also suffered from pain in his feet for years, he enjoyed the attention I was spending on them and told me how good it felt. I told him that the treatment was not specifically for his foot pain but for his shoulder pain. He asked me how it was possible that I could affect his shoulder pain by rubbing his feet. I explained that there were reflex points on his feet that sent energy to various areas of the body. Just as I told him this, my long, thin, but strong fingers found a spot on the outside of his foot near the pinky toe that corresponded to his left shoulder.

He jumped out of the chair about a foot and said, 'Wow! What was that point?'

I smiled confidently and told him that *that* was the shoulder point. The look on my dad's face was like that of a young child sitting on Santa's lap for the first time. His skepticism melted away.

When I finished I felt pure joy in my heart. I had not yet asked my father how he felt, but I knew intuitively what I had done was right and good.

I asked him to get up, do some shoulder rotations, and see how it felt. He stood, moved around a bit, and with a look of wonder in his eyes told me that the pain was completely gone.

'Ted, this stuff is amazing, I'll even help you pay for the course if you need it!'

I continued with the five hundred hours of acupressure courses, which spanned just over a year and half. During this time I moved to the Washington, DC area, but continued to commute home to Massachusetts for the last two weekend trainings. My desire to learn more about Chinese medicine intensified during this time period. So I signed up for a three-year Master's program in acupuncture therapy at the Maryland Institute of Traditional Chinese Medicine. The school was conveniently located in Bethesda, Maryland, which was also just a few minutes from my new home in Northwest DC. I'll never forget finishing my acupressure training on a Sunday evening at six pm in Northampton, Massachusetts. I jumped in the car, drove speedily home to DC, and went to bed just after midnight. I woke the next day at seven am, went to work all day, and began acupuncture school that Monday evening at six pm.

This was the start of a long, passionate journey into learning everything I possibly could about healing the body in the most effective and efficient way possible. However, I soon learned that every healer must first heal himself.

Visiting the South Rim

There I was, lying on the bathroom floor, grasping the edge of the toilet with both hands, completely exhausted, just waiting for the next series of dry heaves to commence.

The year was 1998. I had just begun my second year of acupuncture school. I worked full time during the day, providing nutritional counseling for mothers and children. Then I labored away each night at the Maryland Institute of Traditional Chinese Medicine for three hours until after nine pm.

In the middle of the night, I awoke with a gnawing pain in my abdomen. Exhaustion from work and school deterred me from getting out of bed to address the issue. Hoping the discomfort would soon pass, I tried to fall back asleep. However, the pain and subsequent nausea won out, and I rushed to the bathroom. I kneeled and embraced the toilet until I felt as if I had expelled every last remnant of food from my body. Although it was intense, I felt relieved that whatever bug I obtained had surely passed during this colossal upheaval.

I could now go back to sleep without any more discomfort.

Unfortunately, thirty minutes later, the pain and nausea came back, and I found myself in front of the toilet again. Only this time, there was nothing left to heave but air and bile. This repeated every thirty minutes for the next two hours. Desperately, I combed through my acupuncture book.

I found a point specifically for persistent vomiting. Regrettably, the point had to be on the strangest and most painful area of my body, the veins on the back of the tongue! The directions were simple: needle the veins until they bleed.

Even though I was skeptical and annoyed, I tried it. Standing in the bathroom, dehydrated, exhausted, and nauseous, I stuck a thin needle into the back of my tongue until it bled. It was an unusual experience and it pinched a bit, but I was willing to try anything at that moment. Afterwards, I crawled back into bed, hoping the treatment would bring some relief. I needed sleep so I could get to work rested the next day. I was on a contract position at the time and sick days were not an option. Amazingly, I slept through the night and woke ready to go.

Years later, I discovered that I had hundreds of gallstones in my bile ducts, which was the likely reason that I woke up multiple times a year to vomiting spells. Around this time period, liver issues, intestinal parasites, heavy metal poisoning, yeast overgrowth, chronic fatigue, and irritable bowel syndrome were just some of the many ailments that I suffered through.

Everything changed for me when a Chinese woman came to my acupuncture school to speak to us about the amazing health benefits of qigong. She explained that qigong was a three-thousand-year-old healing system that originated in China. Qigong incorporates slow, rhythmic body movements with gentle breathing patterns. What makes qigong unique is that the movements are accompanied by imagery and visualization. This moving meditation can energize the body and restore vitality. As we reviewed many scientific studies that validated this ancient branch of Chinese medicine, she enlightened us about the numerous diseases that have been successfully treated with qigong. It appeared to be quite an effective therapy for many ailments.

Impressed and inspired, I wanted to learn qigong. I hoped it could help restore some of my vitality and health. However, my days were crammed with school and two jobs, which didn't leave enough time to practice this discipline. Instead, I purchased a couple of books about qigong and tried to sneak in some reading whenever I had a few spare minutes. I recall sitting in acupuncture school during our three hour night classes, slipping in a few pages when the lectures were boring. I read with such enthusiasm and hope of this ancient medicine's healing potential.

Chapter Three:
The Healing Begins

Light Turned On

In 2002, after finishing acupuncture school, I had started my private practice in Bethesda, Maryland. I also consulted at George Washington University's Center for Integrative Medicine in Washington, DC. In this capacity I treated patients and lectured to medical students about energy medicine. Life was good, but I was still dealing with digestive issues, fatigue, and achy joints. Acupuncture, herbs, and other supplements helped me substantially, but I still felt that I could further restore my health. I remembered the lecture about qigong and finally made a concentrated effort to implement this ancient healing discipline into my daily routine.

Healthy people do not need a Doctor.
Sick people do.
I have not come to help the righteous.

Luke 5:31

I found a qigong teacher and started immersing myself into this practice. I performed the qigong meditations every night for an hour before bed. I didn't notice many changes initially, but I still practiced every day without fail. After about a month, I noticed tingling in my hands and feet during the practice, accompanied by warmth in my limbs. My teacher explained that these were normal 'qi' sensations in the body and were all positive indications of a healthy and successful practice.

I had previously suffered from Raynaud's syndrome, which manifests as cold hands and feet. Every winter I endured prickly sensations in my hands that felt like needles digging into my palms. The cold even penetrated through my thickest pair of gloves. However, that winter my circulation dramatically improved. I was stunned when my hands and feet felt completely normal.

After a few months of practicing qigong, springtime finally arrived. I noticed tremendous changes in all aspects of my life. My health, my career, and my financial situation all improved. I remember going out to play tennis with a friend after the long winter ended. I prepared as I usually did by putting on my back and knee braces to help provide warmth to my normally cold, achy joints.

Within just a few minutes of playing, I noticed an unexplained vitality throughout my body. I intuitively felt I no longer needed the braces. So I took them off. For years my braces had been like crutches, and I never considered playing any sport without them. Amazingly, after taking off the braces, I didn't notice any pain. My lower back and knee joints felt like they had new life.

After an hour—my previous limit before I got fatigued—my friend asked if I wanted to call it quits. I told him, 'No, let's keep going, I feel pretty good!'

We played for over two hours that day and I never became fatigued. More importantly, there was no hint of joint pain. This was remarkable, because joint pain had been my constant companion since I was twenty-three. Finally, at the age of thirty-three, I was free of the pain that had so deeply interfered with my life.

I felt blessed to regain my physical health. Yet nothing prepared me for the shifts I experienced emotionally. Having suffered from social anxiety all my life, I now possessed a more relaxed nature. My confidence and self-esteem soared, and I felt happy and full of life.

As my vitality rose, I participated in more and more activities. I worked out at the gym, took up basketball again, and played a lot of tennis. One day I met a man at the courts who invited me to join his United States Tennis Association (USTA) team. I'd never played organized tennis before, but decided to give it a shot.

Even though I lacked tennis skills, playing it for fun more than competition, my qigong practice boosted my level of play. Practices were tough and I tried to learn as much as I could from my teammates.

On the day of my first regulation match, I had tons of energy and was athletic enough to get the ball back over the net one more time than my opponent. Often, the games would be lengthy because each point took so long. I couldn't hit winners past my opponent, yet I always was able to return the ball back over the court no matter where my opponent hit it. I felt like I could run forever. Somehow I went undefeated and led my team into the Maryland USTA state playoffs.

In the last match at the state final, I ran into my twin, who was also undefeated. We played the same grinding style of play that wore out our opponents. Our teams played five separate matches and we were tied two to two. This meant that my match decided the teams' fate. The winners advanced to the Mid-Atlantic round, which preceded the elusive National tournament.

After three hours of play, my opponent and I were deadlocked. My entire team anxiously crowded the sideline awaiting the outcome. In between games, my opponent and I chatted for a few moments. I stood by the net, feeling crisp and energetic, while he slumped in the chair on the sideline. He looked at me with a curious eye and said, 'You know, I usually win by outlasting my opponents. I can't believe you're not tired at all!'

I just smiled and made some random friendly comment.

My daily qigong exercises gave me abundant vitality. When I once explained this to a friend, he equated this energy to getting amped up on caffeine. But the energy that comes from qigong isn't the jittery kind. The ample energy comes with a stable, grounded feeling. Quite simply, I never got tired but still slept like a baby at night.

So, after three and a half hours of a two set tennis match, I ground out another victory simply by having more energy than my now exhausted opponent. As I walked off the court, elbows bloodied from a couple of dives, my team congratulated me. My team captain even gave me a big hug, and he wasn't the hugging type. We ended up moving on and winning the Mid-Atlantic region and then went to Tucson for the National tournament, losing to the eventual champion, Texas. My teammates affectionately gave me the nickname 'Three-Hour Ted' because of my long-lasting style of play. Little did they know that just a year prior I could barely have lasted an hour on the tennis court.

By restoring my health, qigong changed my life. I felt like a new being. My lifelong social anxiety issues melted away, as did other excessive emotions like anger, worry, and fear. Most people who know me today recognize me as a carefree, relaxed individual.

My daily qigong practice not only bred physical and emotional rewards but spiritual benefits. I developed a deeper passion for spiritual pursuits. I experienced a stronger connection with God, and felt better able to lead a proper Christian lifestyle.

My ability to be compassionate to my 'neighbor' strengthened, and I learned to use prayer and meditation to transform my thought patterns from negative to positive.

As I blended various Eastern practices such as yoga, meditation, and qigong into my daily routine, I began to develop a much greater understanding of these esoteric practices and exactly how they affected the body, mind, and spirit. Before, 'yoga' and 'meditation' were just faddish catchphrases to me, but when I used them they brought a new outlook and meaning to my life. More so, they helped me gain a greater understanding of myself and of God.

My newfound health and vitality was simple, it came from the massive amount of energy that I was cultivating through my qigong practice. *Qi*, translated, means energy, spirit, or life force. *Gong* means work or cultivation. Therefore, *qigong* is the art and practice of energy cultivation within the body. Through my qigong practice and studies I became familiar with a significant energy center in our body, which the Daoists call the lower dantian. This energy center is in every human being and acts as a reservoir or collecting point for life force or qi within the body. Quite simply, the lower dantian is like a battery that can store energy for health and healing. Years prior, if someone told me that there was an invisible energy center in the lower abdomen just below the naval I may have pooh-poohed the notion. However, by experiencing the meridian system years earlier, I had come to fully believe in an energetic anatomy that exists within our bodies. More so, I always noticed the warmth in my lower abdomen after practicing qigong cultivation exercises for an hour or more. When I explain the lower dantian to people, I compare it to our cell phones. Our cell phones have numerous applications and functions that help get us through each busy day. Most of us make a point to charge our cells phones at least once daily. We know full well that this wonderful device is completely useless without adequate power to fuel the applications.

Our bodies are no different. We require significant amounts of energy daily for the thousands of processes that occur within us. I have come to believe that my body functions at a much higher level when I perform my daily qigong exercises. I am happier, healthier, and full of energy and spirit.

In the Far East, they use qigong for many purposes, with the main intent being to promote optimal health and prevent disease. Martial artists and athletes use it to increase their stamina and improve their physical abilities. Many of the famous martial artists that you see demonstrating supernatural feats are also qigong masters who have used these meditative techniques to master the art of fighting and self-defense. Daoist and Buddhist monks use qigong breathing techniques as part of their meditative practices for purely spiritual purposes.

From a Daoist perspective, by using qigong to energize the body, one can then further energize the spirit as well.

Another means in which people use qigong is for healing others, using the cultivated qi energy that one obtains from the exercises and using it to heal others who are sick. This is referred to as medical qigong and is gaining popularity in the United States at a rapid pace.

Chapter Four:
Laying On of Hands

As my health continued to improve, my yearning for knowledge about healing escalated. I wanted to learn more about the spiritual and energetic aspects of healing as my insatiable thirst for wisdom grew. In 2003, a year before studying medical qigong, I was in San Francisco, California taking a three-day qigong training with another Daoist master, Mantak Chia, from Thailand. Master Chia often visited the U.S. to conduct trainings, this time on the campus of San Francisco State University.

During this time, I stayed with my older sister Annemarie, who lives in the Bay area. My main desire for this journey was to obtain as much knowledge about qigong as I possibly could. In addition to the

Jesus went through all of the towns and villages, teaching in their synagogues, proclaiming the good news of the kingdom and healing every disease and sickness.

Matthew 9:35

weekend training, I wanted to visit a few Traditional Chinese Medicine schools (TCM) and also tap other resources such as clinics and bookstores. Outside of China, California is a hotbed for anything related to Chinese medicine and I wanted to take advantage of my time in San Francisco and specifically, Chinatown.

So I visited several schools of acupuncture and Chinese medicine and went directly to their libraries in search for rare texts on qigong. One librarian led me to the section on qigong and I slowly began scanning each shelf for a comprehensive volume. My eyes widened as I looked up on the top row of shelves and spotted a three-inch thick brown book that had the words *Medical Qigong Therapy* printed on the spine. I stood in the aisle perusing the 500-page masterpiece for over an hour with my jaw hanging down close to the floor in pure wonderment.

After extracting myself from this awestruck state, I darted to the front desk and asked the librarian if the book was for sale. She said no but told me that I could find it in Chinatown at Eastwind Bookstore.

I jumped in my car, drove to Chinatown, found the store, and purchased Dr. Jerry Alan Johnson's *Chinese Medical Qigong Therapy: A Comprehensive Text*. It was the best $120 I've ever spent. After immersing myself in the text for months, I reached an inevitable conclusion. I knew that I would go back to California the next year to study under Dr. Johnson to become certified as a medical qigong therapist.

Dr. Jerry Alan Johnson is the only known non-Asian qigong master in the West. His training in internal martial arts (healing) began with an interest in external martial arts (fighting) as a child. In his twenties, he became a champion martial arts fighter. This was in the 1970s and 80s, but eventually he transitioned into only using his skills to heal others. Like many who become interested in Chinese medicine, he first learned acupuncture, then steeped himself into the deeper and more esoteric branch of Chinese energetic medicine, qigong. Because of his recognition as a fighter, he gained credence among many Asian masters. This trust enabled Dr. Johnson to learn more than the average person and become privy to secret teachings of spiritual and energetic medicine from qigong masters from the East. He trained in China in the early 1990s at several well-regarded TCM training centers and treated patients at the Medical Qigong Clinic at the Xi Yuan Hospital of Traditional Chinese Medicine. After earning a license as a Doctor of Traditional Chinese Medicine, he launched the first medical qigong school in the U.S. in 1997. I began my training with Dr. Johnson at the International Institute of Medical Qigong in Pacific Grove, California in 2004.

Energy Sensitive

I enjoyed studying and practicing energy medicine with such talented healers, and was I intrigued by how many students were already so naturally gifted at this work. Many who are attracted to energy healing are already blessed with psychic gifts and can feel energy more than the average person. My teacher would refer to these naturally gifted folks as 'energy sensitive.' I did not fall into this category. When I hovered my hand over a person's body while scanning or diagnosing during some of the medical qigong protocols, I usually didn't feel much at all. However, I continued my studies that year. I knew that with continued training I could improve my energetic sensitivity.

Months after I completed my training in California, I was in Gettysburg treating a regular acupuncture patient of mine named Evelyn. Evelyn was in her late sixties, overweight, with diabetes, arthritis, and pain in just about every joint in her body. She came every couple of weeks for acupuncture to relieve her discomfort. While I treated her, she spoke her mind freely in a frenetic manner. She enjoyed the treatments and I enjoyed her blunt, honest nature.

Evelyn and I shared a curiosity about self-help to cure the body. I was always eager to teach her about herbs, nutritional supplements, stretching exercise, and other methods to help her heal. However, I hesitated to suggest qigong breathing exercises, medical qigong treatments, or yoga postures, because she was a Catholic and I didn't want to offend her or scare her away. Just a few months prior, a patient had become fearful when I suggested medical qigong, claiming that it was 'New Age medicine' and went against her Christian values.

So I suggested some breathing exercises that originated from qigong philosophy but were also universal enough that I wasn't crossing any boundaries. Although Evelyn took the Chinese herbal formulas I offered her, she, for whatever reason, didn't practice the breathing exercises. Over the years as a therapist, I've learned that it's important to only prescribe what the patient can process.

Some time later, Evelyn brought her fifteen-year-old grandson, Logan, in to the clinic during one of her acupuncture sessions. Logan was very friendly, always having a smile on his face, but was very shy. Whenever I asked him how he was doing I was lucky to get more than one word out of him.

Logan suffered from a paralyzing amount of anxiety. Anytime he got within a few hundred feet of his school he had a panic attack. Evelyn asked me if there was anything I could do for him. Oddly, this pattern ran in the family, as Logan's mother and Evelyn herself had this same issue with anxiety around going to school. Although Logan was an exceptional student and enjoyed school very much, the anxiety became so bad that he physically could not go anymore. I really wanted to help him.

I thought medical qigong therapy could help to alleviate Logan's anxiety. Using medical qigong, one can dip into the patient's body, sense and feel the emotional blockage, and remove turbid emotions from the body. This can often free the patient of the distressing feelings. However, thinking that I might offend them by suggesting this treatment option, I conservatively suggested that acupuncture alone could be helpful. They agreed, and we began treatment for him.

After about two sessions there was no change in Logan's anxiety. He continued to be tutored from home and not able to go to school. While I was treating Evelyn, she and I were continuing our discussion about Logan's issues when suddenly she asked me, 'What about that Kung Fu energy stuff that you do, would that help Logan at all?'

Stunned that she would even suggest that, I opportunely responded, 'Yes, absolutely! If you think he's open to trying it?'

So after treating Evelyn, I took Logan into the treatment room and explained to him that I would be doing some acupuncture but adding some energy work to the session. After explaining medical qigong to him, I asked if he was willing to give it a try. He agreed and we started the treatment. When I began working on Logan I was confident that I could assist the release of his anxiety.

I started the session with a short meditation and prayer to connect myself to the divine. I stood with my eyes closed in front of Logan as he lay on the massage table in front of me.

I asked Jesus for love, light, and protection, rooted myself, and then began the treatment by scanning Logan's body. Starting at his feet, I slowly hovered my hands six inches above Logan's body. When I reached his torso, I decreased my pace even more. I listened and felt what his body was presenting to me.

In Chinese medicine the area around the solar plexus is referred to as the yellow court, which is an energetic center where a person's unresolved emotional energies can stagnate. I believe this is why, when we experience emotional pain from a traumatic or stressful event, we often describe it feeling as if we've been punched in the gut.

Eventually, his solar plexus radiated heat that caused a sensation in my palm. I initially wrote it off as my hand brushing against his shirt, although it was not. Then I thought maybe a slight itch was manifesting in my hand. Even though as an energy healer I had been taught to expect these sensations, I was astonished, and my analytical mind was seeking a physical explanation.

The sensations intensified as if I had uncovered a pot of steaming hot water and the heat was coming into my hand. It wasn't as hot as steam and it wasn't wet, but the intensity of the feeling was similar.

As this energy continued to flow out of Logan's body and upward toward my hand, I became excited. This was one of the first times I felt significant energy while doing medical qigong on a patient. Yet I could tell that this energy possessed an unhealthy nature and needed to be removed. It wasn't something I wanted in my body and I certainly didn't want Logan to absorb again. So I quickly disposed of it by tossing it into the earth to be recycled.

As I continued to purge this toxic energy from Logan for several minutes, he seemed to drift off into a world of peaceful relaxation. Here I was, removing all this filthy emotional stagnation from his body, and he looked like he was lying on a beach in the sun.

I didn't know exactly what this energy was, but sensed intuitively that it was related to some emotional event in Logan's life or possibly a series of emotional events. I instinctively felt that removing it was going to be helpful in resolving some of Logan's anxiety issues. I could feel his body becoming lighter and lighter as I continued to purge undesirable energies from his body for several minutes.

After his body finished releasing and I no longer felt the turbid energy coming out of him, I finished the treatment. I had Logan get up off the table and asked if he felt different in any way. Logan, a man of few words, merely said that he felt more relaxed.

Most patients don't realize the full effect of acupuncture or qigong treatments until a day or two after the session as things start to settle. So I waited until our next appointment and asked him again. Logan reported feeling less anxious.

I continued to treat him several times more with medical qigong. Each time Logan felt better and better, and within about three weeks he was able to go back to school. This change in Logan's nature greatly pleased his grandmother and she was very grateful.

I was thankful, too—for the opportunity to learn, to be able to add another modality to help people with emotional issues, and that Evelyn and Logan had showed their trust not just in me but also in Chinese medicine. This was the first of a series of miracles to come within my personal practice of energy medicine.

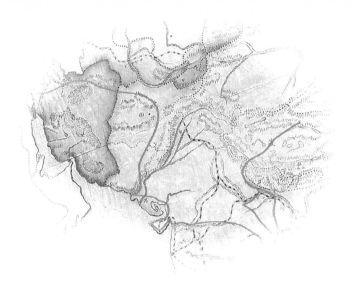

Chapter Five:
The Missing Years of Jesus

George and the Mustard Seed Library

The more I learned about healing and Eastern medicine, the more I started seeing correlations between healers of all kinds. In 2000 I went through many transitions in my life. I was finishing my last clinical hours at acupuncture school, cramming for my national certification exam, and going through a tough breakup with a girlfriend with whom I had lived for many years. We were in Northwest DC at the time and I was seeking a new residence. I decided to look just over the district line in Bethesda, Maryland, since the rents were cheaper and my school and work were there, too.

Where did this man get this
wisdom and these miraculous powers?

Matthew 13:54

I moved into the home of man who lived alone but rented out several rooms in his large Bethesda house, which was very close to the National Institutes of Health (NIH) campus. George was an eccentric in his late sixties with a white beard and a bellowing laugh who walked with stiff, deliberate movements, his portly belly held out before him. I could imagine him in a red suit, a perfect Santa Claus.

At our first meeting, he told me he was some sort of Christian minister for the Bethesda Unity Church. Initially I felt unsure about living in this odd man's home. Newly single, I wanted to move in with people my own age and spread my wings. But intuitively I felt comfortable with George. Moving into his place would offer the comfort and rest I needed at that time in my life. I figured that his home might provide a safer haven for me to recuperate physically as well as spiritually.

George offered different weekly groups at his home and always asked politely if I wanted to join in. I always respectfully declined. He respected my wish not to wander from my Catholic faith. Nevertheless, George and I still shared meaningful conversations about Jesus and God on occasion.

During this time period I was just beginning to study and read more about qigong healing and how masters from the East executed their healings. One day I was in the living room with a friend who is also an acupuncturist and qigong practitioner.

We were discussing the idea of Jesus traveling East during his lifetime to study and teach. We both noticed the remarkable similarities between the healing abilities of Jesus Christ and of many of the saints and yogis from the East. A large gap in Jesus' lifetime was unaccounted for, and we wondered if Jesus could have traveled during that time. Without supporting evidence, these were just speculations.

Then George walked in through the front door and overheard our conversation while lugging groceries into the kitchen. He came back through the living room, stood there in his button-down nylon shirt, and said, 'You know, Jesus really did spend time in India.'

'Really?' I wanted to know more. He answered my questions matter-of-factly. I was excited, but also skeptical. Could this story actually be true? If so, then why didn't more people know about it? Could it be possible that the information had been lost or suppressed?

Still skeptical but interested, I examined the evidence about Jesus in India. There had to be books and documentaries about this subject. Sure enough, I immersed myself in the 'Mustard Seed Library,' a room in his house George dedicated to his students for higher learning. I watched compelling videos and read books such as *Jesus in India, The Lost Years of Jesus Christ,* and *The Life of Saint Issa.* Over the next few months this became a minor obsession, and I continued my studies at the local Barnes and Noble bookstore.

I found the story so well documented, with so much evidence, that only one skeptical question remained: Why didn't the Bible contain this information about Jesus' life?

The Mystical Beginning to Jesus' Life

Even before Jesus Christ entered into the world, miracles showed how special his life would become: the visits from angels foretelling the fate of Mary, Joseph, and the rest of the world. Reading the Bible, I get a sense of magnitude and divine inspiration around Jesus' arrival. Jesus' birth was filled with miracles and displayed an injection of the Holy Spirit. First, Mary conceived Jesus despite being a virgin. Both Jesus' parents, Mary and Joseph, were distressed by the pregnancy but later comforted by angels that visited them. These divine beings assured Mary and Joseph that Jesus was sent by God and was to be very special.

When Jesus finally does arrive under extremely humble circumstances, there are even more miraculous occurrences as more angels come down from the heavens to deliver messages to the people that Jesus was born the Son of God.

After Jesus' birth, shepherds in the fields and wise men from the East were also divinely guided to the small, humble town called Bethlehem to witness the birth of a new King. Even the currently enthroned Herod, who had heard about this 'newborn king,' was roused by the news—so much that he immediately wanted this newborn to be found and killed!

Right from the start, it was clear that this individual was special, and that his life on earth would be remarkable and well documented. By age twelve, this prodigy had evolved to preaching the word of God in the Temple in illuminating fashion.

I've watched documentary films about the life of Jesus. When I see Jesus at age twelve, preaching in the Temple, my mouth salivates as I await what the next scene unveils. Each time I'm disappointed that the story unexpectedly comes to an abrupt halt. There's not a bit of information about what Jesus did during a span of well over fifteen years. The Bible mentions that Jesus 'increased in wisdom and stature and in favor with God and man' (Luke 2:52) but does not say how or where.

Depictions of Jesus' life show him returning to Jerusalem at the river Jordan, being baptized. John the Baptist, stunned and barely recognizing Jesus, blesses him. He realizes that he is to 'decrease' and Jesus is to 'increase' as the Holy Spirit comes down from the heavens and speak, confirming this notion (John 3:30). Jesus' mother Mary, as depicted in the 2013 movie *Son of God*, is elated when she is informed that Jesus has finally returned home at age twenty-nine. The Bible describes how others were shocked and awestruck to see a man, who they remembered as a relatively ordinary twelve-year-old, performing all sorts of miracles and displaying extraordinary wisdom.

Many have speculated and books have been written about where Jesus was during this time period. Yet the Bible does not specify where he went or what he did during the time period between ages thirteen and twenty-nine. We only know that, wherever he was, he 'grew in wisdom and in stature and in favor with God and man.'

Did Jesus grow in wisdom and in stature and in favor with God and man by quietly building bookshelves and houses for nearly twenty years? Many theologians and historians assume that Jesus lived a simple life as a carpenter with his father Joseph. However, there is little to no evidence to support this notion.

This period is often referred to as the 'lost' or 'missing' years of Jesus Christ.

As I gained insights into how the Eastern masters performed healing miracles, I pondered the possibility of a connection between Jesus and these gurus. At first, I didn't believe that Jesus had spent time in India and Tibet. But the Bible had many 'gospels' that didn't make the final cut. Were the scrolls found in India that documented Jesus' life simply another gospel that didn't end up in the final version of the Bible?

Life of Saint Issa

Russian researcher Nicholas Notovitch, an aristocrat and journalist, introduced the most prominent evidence that placed Jesus in India and Tibet. In the 1880s, Notovitch embarked on an extended journey through the Orient.

While traveling, Notovitch broke a leg, which forced him to remain under care of the Buddhist monks at the Hemis monastery in Kashmir for an extended period. The extreme altitude of over 14,000 feet and the arduous trek to reach the monastery made it a difficult place to visit at the time of Notovitch's travels.

During this time, Notovitch learned of ancient records, written in the Tibetan Pali language, of the life of Jesus Christ. The head lama allowed him to see and translate these scrolls, titled *The Life of Saint Issa*. Issa translated in Farsi means Jesus. These records corresponded to the life of Jesus Christ from birth until his death, including details of how he lived from age twelve to twenty-nine.

In 1894, after returning from his journey, Notovitch published his book, called *The Unknown Life of Christ*. Although it attracted much interest, many questioned its authenticity and called it a hoax. Notovitch stood by his claims and encouraged a further scientific excursion to validate the existence of the scrolls. Since then, many skeptics have traveled to Hemis monastery to debunk Notovitch's story.

All left convinced that the scrolls were authentic. Several wrote their own books about their experience.

After reading just about every book and website and hearing all accounts of Jesus' possible visit East, I formulated a new theory of what Jesus did and where he 'increased in wisdom' during these years.

Today, when I watch documentaries about Jesus' life, I close my eyes right after the scene of him in the Temple at age twelve. I then visualize what I believe truly happened in the next sixteen years:

After his edifying discourses at the temple, Jesus' reputation grew, and his parents' home became a meeting place for the distinguished and wealthy. Many saw Jesus as the future king and the perfect son-in-law. Uncomfortable with the fame, Jesus planned an escape towards the Far East in the middle of the night. Jesus' goal was to fulfill his prophesy by perfecting himself in the law of the great Buddhas.

In a train of merchants traveling along the Silk Road, the famed trade route connecting China and the Mediterranean, Jesus crossed through Persia, Afghanistan, and Pakistan. He then crossed the Sindh into Midwestern India. From there he traversed India to Odisha and arrived in Jagannath, where the well-known Shree Jagannath Temple still stands today. Jagannath has been a renowned center of Hindu learning for centuries. He studied and taught with the White Priests and Jain monks for several years and learned to heal and expel evil desires from man. Everywhere young Jesus traveled, he was welcomed as his reputation grew.

Traditionally in India, a caste system existed and still is in place today. The higher class White Priests and warriors (Brahmins and Kshatriyas) did not associate with the lower class (Shudras). Jesus disregarded this social stratification system and tended to spend most of his time with the sick and lower caste people.

The White Priests expressed their disapproval with this behavior as tensions grew. Eventually, they sought to eliminate Jesus as his power grew. Jesus was warned by the Shudras of their plan and escaped at night, heading north towards the mountainous regions.

Jesus spent five years in the Himalayan Mountains, between Nepal and Kashmir, in deep meditation. After a full awakening of his psychic and healing abilities, he eventually journeyed back to Palestine to meet his destiny in Jerusalem.

One of the first to attempt a visit to Hemis Monastery to discredit Notovitch was Swami Abhedanandaa, a leading figure in the Ramakrishna Society. In 1922, he visited the monastery, confirmed the documents' existence, and also had them translated. He later published his translations of the Issa scriptures in his book, titled *Kashmir O Tibbate*.

The famous Russian artist and intellectual Nicholas Roerich visited the Hemis monastery in 1925, and published his account of the translations of the manuscripts in his books *Heart of Asia* and *Altai-Himalaya*. His account and translations, like Abhedanandaa's, match Notovich's story.

Many other well-respected individuals have visited Hemis over the years and confirming the existence of the scrolls, including U.S. Supreme Court Justice William O. Douglas in 1951. In his book, *Beyond the High Himalayas*, he observed that there were many legends in the area concerning the monastery at Hemis, and that one of them related to Jesus.

As my interest in the possibility that Jesus traveled to India grew, my desire to visit India increased as well. I already was developing a general interest in Indian culture, their cuisine, and of course their deep traditions and knowledge about healing. I specifically wanted to learn more about the practices of yoga and meditation as well. So, in 2007 I finally took time to go to India for an entire month.

I arrived in the large city of New Delhi and stayed with some Indian friends for a few days. There were lots of people, lots of traffic, lots of noise, and lots of pollution. I was anxious to make my way to Rishikesh, a small town in the foothills of the Himalayas nestled along the sacred Ganges River. Rishikesh is known for its deep history of yoga and spirituality and has been referred to as the yoga capital of the world. Even the Beatles visited Rishikesh back in the 1970s, staying at one of the many local ashrams to immerse themselves in yoga and meditation.

Some popular ashrams are situated right in town along the river, while others are found along the hills high above the river and off the beaten path. I took a train from New Delhi headed north to Haridwar, then took a bus to Rishikesh and finally a rickshaw to the ashram where I was to stay for a few weeks. While hiking on the long path up the hill to the ashram I came across several monkeys, which are commonplace in India. Thanks to the tip in the Lonely Planet guide, I pretended to pick some rocks from the ground to throw. The monkeys scattered at once.

My dorm room contained a desk, a chair, and a steel-framed bed with a mattress and a couple of sheets. A glass lamp on the ceiling shone onto the concrete floor. The adjoining bathroom had only cold running water.

I sat on the bed with pillow against the wall and studied the rule sheets and daily routine. Each day we would meet before sunrise for meditation, followed by yoga then breakfast. In the late afternoon and evening we would do the same. However, during the daytime we often had freedom to leave the premises and explore a bit. A younger man who I became acquainted with at the ashram asked if I wanted to visit a famous cave just North of Rishikesh. Aware of the many legends of Eastern masters, yogis, and saints that have spent *years* of their life meditating in seclusion, I eagerly agreed to accompany him on the excursion.

Vashishta Cave, named after the famous sage who had spent years meditating in the cave, has become home to many other yogis over the centuries. When we arrived, we walked down a long fenced-in walkway towards a small ashram, which sat along the banks of the Ganges River. As we approached we saw a small shed-like building to the right of the ashram, which was flush against the wall of the adjacent mountainside. This was the entrance to the renowned cave. My friend and I went into it respectfully as other visitors sat praying outside on a bench. We walked and eventually crawled deeper into the cave as we approached a small shrine with a couple of candles burning. We each found a spot on the rocks to sit comfortably and meditate for a few minutes.

Typically I struggle to find a quiescent state of mind while meditating. Being in the cave that day was an unusual experience for me as my mind immediately entered a tranquil state. There seemed to be a unique energy or presence that we both felt as we sat in stillness. I only wish I could bottle that atmosphere for my daily meditations at home!

Afterwards, blinded by the sunlight while exiting the cave, we briefly visited the ashram next door. We were able to meet and chat with the swami that lived there. A humble man of about forty years of age with short brown hair and a peaceful smile, he willingly chatted with us for a few minutes. We asked him many questions about what it was like being in a remote ashram along the Ganges all his life. He shared with us a story of how he once made a visit to the United States. He enjoyed the visit very much but felt like a fish out of water and was anxious to return home to Rishikesh.

Noticing that we were both Westerners and enthusiastic to be visiting the legendary cave, the swami informed of us another less-traveled cave of interest. The 'Jesus Cave' is an unmarked cave set in the side of a steep hill along the banks of the Ganges River just a bit downstream from the ashram.

The swami informed us of a legend that Jesus had spent time in this cave during his travels to India two thousand years prior. According to tradition, many Hindu saints and yogis have had visions of Jesus Christ visiting India. Both Swami Rama Tirtha (1873-1906) and Swami Papa Ramdas (1884-1963) lived at the cave in separate eras. Despite not knowing of Jesus' travels to India prior to their visits, they both reported having distinct visions of Jesus meditating there.

After walking along the rocky banks about ten minutes, we came upon the auspicious site. We then zealously scurried up the small cliff to enter the cave. The view from there was even more awesome with the river and a backdrop of Himalayan peaks.

I could not verify whether or not Jesus had actually meditated in the place where I sat that day. However, simply knowing that I was sitting in a cave in the remote areas of the Himalayas where Jesus may have set foot moved me considerably. The thought of unintentionally tracing Jesus' actual footsteps in India was humbling indeed.

The story of Jesus traveling to India and studying with the Buddhists and Hindus may seem shocking at first. Many believe that since Jesus was born the Son of God, he already possessed the wisdom and healing gifts and didn't need training.

What we do know from the Bible is that wherever Jesus was, he did indeed gain in knowledge and skill. We also know that before Jesus left Galilee at age twelve, he didn't yet possess his miraculous healing abilities. When he arrived back on the scene at age twenty-nine, he was an evolved master, healing an array of diseases and performing supernatural feats. Even the Pharisees were surprised at Jesus' abilities and wondered where he gained these skills. It seems likely that Jesus did require some additional knowledge and training to fully awaken his divine skills. What we do not know is *how* and *where* he acquired these skills.

Since healing and spirituality have a long and great tradition in the East, it seems like a logical place for Jesus to have increased in wisdom and ability. For him to have traveled to India is the best-documented and evidenced-based story about Jesus during these years of his life. Still, whether or not Jesus traveled to the East wasn't important to me. What did matter was that I felt as if I was slowly putting together pieces to a puzzle that had intrigued me since I was a child.

In 1964, Pope Paul VI opened the doors to Eastern religions as a sign of respect and to promote interfaith relationships with other spiritual traditions. Many well-respected Christians have utilized Eastern teachings before and since, in efforts to enhance their relationship with Jesus and invoke healing abilities. Maybe Jesus was doing this long before Pope Paul VI's declaration.

In the East, there are specific meditative techniques to attain union with God. It is this same kingdom of God that Jesus encourages us to strive for in our lives. Could these missing years of his life unlock the secret of how Jesus attained union himself?

Chapter Six:
Is Energy Healing Un-Christian?

A patient with back and hip pain came to me for acupuncture years ago. After a few sessions, she felt better, and asked if I did anything for depression and anxiety. I told her that acupuncture could help, but suggested medical qigong to more effectively release the underlying emotional energy.

Since she seemed confused as to what medical qigong was, I explained that it was a form of hands-on energy healing similar to reiki. She shrugged and asked if medical qigong was some sort of 'New Age' medicine. I clarified that medical qigong had been around for thousands of years and was scientifically proven to be helpful for many health conditions. She turned down the offer, because she felt

And these signs shall follow them that believe; in my name they shall lay their hands on the sick, and they shall recover.

Mark 16:17-18

it was against her Christian faith to receive such treatment. She opted to have just acupuncture treatment. I didn't push her or question her choice, although I was surprised that anyone would consider this work un-Christian.

Afterwards, I did some research and discovered that many Christians have issues with energy healing. Many think that it is spiritually dangerous and healing is an act only to be initiated by God himself. Some assume this type of medicine is unhealthy, simply because they do not trust or understand it. Some even believe that energy healing to be the work of Satan, and practitioners of this work must be avoided at all costs.

But what could be more 'Christian' than wanting to help another person and ease their physical or emotional pain? Based on my vast experience as an energy healer and a Christian, I truly believe that Jesus Christ smiles when he sees one of his children here on earth laying their hands on another being in attempt to alleviate suffering as he did.

Every person that I've met in this field of medicine has displayed the good-hearted intention of sincerely wanting to help other human beings end their suffering.

In addition, many Christians today, at all levels of the Catholic Church and in other denominations, practice energy healing modalities such as acupuncture, reiki, and medical qigong. Many Christians view energy healing modalities as a natural extension of their Christian faith.

In my opinion, there are few better ways to express love to another human being than to lay your hands on them or over them to make them happy and healthy again.

There are many forms of healthcare in the world. One may choose Western medicine in the form of drugs or surgery, or holistic forms of healing such as herbs, nutritional supplements, or dietary changes. Still others incorporate various forms of exercise, like running, biking, walking, or weight lifting to maintain their health.

Yet the mention of the word 'energy' in relation to healing makes many people uncomfortable.

Jesus was the Son of God and his healings were miraculous. I believe that God has a hand in all healing, whether it be by a mother's hug, a prescription medication, an acupuncture treatment, a change in diet, or surgery. I feel that we should not discriminate between the various forms of healing that are available in the world if they are safe and effective.

Who is the one giving the hug or performing the surgery or administering the treatment? It's any person and we have a gift from God called free will. All of us here on earth do and we let this free will play out on God's playground every day. We can choose to sin, commit crime, or hurt others; or to show our love and help others and try to heal. God assists us if we call on him, but we are ultimately the drivers of the car and determine where our soul focuses its energy with our God-given gift of free will.

When I walk into the treatment room. I call on Jesus to assist me. I ask for his guidance and protection and for his light and love to flow through me while I treat someone. I feel that God is always the source of energy and light but I am the director of the show, and it's up to me to call on God for assistance. I am the one who made the choice to heal, even though I am using God's tools while I work.

Some people regard energy healing techniques like reiki and medical qigong as un-Christian simply because they stem from other religions. However, in Vatican II Pope Paul VI sought interfaith dialogue with other religions and their meditative practices, encouraging us to embrace the truth in these religions and learn to take aspects of their teachings to enhance our Christian faith. Many within the Catholic hierarchy have used Eastern healing modalities such as meditation and yoga for centuries to promote their own health and that of their patients and loved ones.

When people consider healing unsafe or evil, this conviction comes from fear and ignorance. If people simply looked closer at the science of energy medicine and took more steps to understand what it is and what it can do, I feel they would soon embrace it fully.

This understanding is already spreading. Hospitals and medical clinics are bringing more holistic therapies into the conventional realm; most major medical schools now offer courses in energy healing techniques including acupuncture, herbs, qigong, and reiki. Energy medicine also gains a lot of media attention. In fact, energy medicine and the growing interest in the 'body, mind, spirit' connection is not a fad but a fast-growing movement and a realization that people are beginning to understand, which is that the body is much more than just physical tissue.

When I run into someone who tells me acupuncture is quackery, voodoo, or 'all in the head,' I point out that they are now in the minority. Science has proven many times over that acupuncture works. The popularity and acceptance of this field of medicine will continue to grow. As the misunderstandings and prejudice vanish, I expect followers of Christian religions to embrace these techniques more and more.

Here's something worth remembering: when Jesus laid his hands on people to heal them, many thought it was the work of the devil. He was eventually murdered due to others' fear and ignorance.

Jesus came to us two thousand years ago to show us how it was to be done. He encouraged us to heal others as he did. Here we are in the 21st century, still condemning those who wish to replicate

Jesus' works, simply because we do not understand or believe in their methods.

What is Healing?

To examine whether energy healing is un-Christian, let's first consider what exactly healing is and what it isn't.

The human body has an incredible ability to heal itself. For many of us, our first 'healing' happened when we scraped our knee playing outside. We ran inside to our mother, crying, and she began the healing process with intention, a big loving hug and an affirmation that everything was going to be okay. She probably cleaned and disinfected the wound and applied some lotion to promote faster healing, finishing the job with a Band-Aid, a kiss, and one more affirmation that everything was 'all better!' From there, the body took over the healing process, and our God-given healing powers rebuilt the injured tissues. Within just a few weeks, the knee was back to normal, healed.

The human body has an innate ability to restore its whole state. God created our bodies this way and it's miraculous to witness. However, many ailments need intervention to heal fully. For example, a broken leg may call for surgery, heart disease and diabetes may require dietary and lifestyle changes, and depression and anxiety may ease with counseling. Even the scraped knee benefited from cleaning, bandaging, and love from Mom.

As an acupuncturist and energy healer, I insert ultra-thin needles at various locations on the body to promote healing in my patients. I put them along meridians where the body's energy pools and stagnates. This stagnation can create imbalance, which then leads to pain, discomfort, and emotional turbulence. Time and time again I've witnessed clients coming into my clinic in pain and leaving with the pain having vanished. I don't put any medication on the needles, the needles simply stimulate the body's own innate healing potential.

By simply stimulating your own body's energy and removing the blockages, much like a farmer diverts waterways in order for his crops to grow, you can help your body heal itself more quickly and naturally. After twenty years of practicing this art, I'm still amazed how the body can heal itself when given the proper stimulation and a few properly placed stainless steel needles.

We may think of a 'healing' as some superhuman feat where someone comes back from the dead, a blind man gains sight, or a life-long paralytic walks moments after getting touched by holy person. But in reality we are healing all the time.

Our bodies can develop disease at any time based on genetic factors, dietary factors, lifestyle choices, emotional challenges, traumas, and injuries.

Although our bodies can heal themselves, they often need love, attention, support, and knowledge from an outside source to awaken this healing potential.

The other day at the barbershop, my friend Dave asked how I was doing and I mentioned that I was writing a book about healing. He then asked me, 'Well, isn't all healing supposed to come from God?'

I said I believed everything comes from God, including the gift of healing. As we chatted he asked in a mildly sarcastic tone, 'Have you ever healed anyone, Ted?'

I told him about the many people who came to me in pain, benefited from my treatments, and ultimately were healed. His sarcastic tone escalated a tad as he suggested that maybe I was some sort of saint, considering this ability.

I pointed out that I was like any other conventional or holistic therapist or physician. Healers come in different forms, and we all promote health and well-being. I wasn't doing anything special or different.

Energy is Everything

Over the years, I've made dozens of presentations to various groups about acupuncture and energy medicine. Whether I am speaking to third-year medical students at George Washington University about qigong or to 5th graders at an elementary school about acupuncture, I always start my lectures off with the same question.

'What is energy?'

No matter what age and education level, I always get the same reaction: blank stares.

I then ask my audience what color is energy, what is its shape, and what does it feel like?

More blank stares.

I then remind my audience that the word energy is a noun; it's found in every dictionary and it's certainly a real thing. We put gas in our cars for energy, we put food in our mouth for energy, we pay our electric bills and heating bills for energy. The sun gives plants and our bodies energy and without energy we wouldn't survive. Everything we do is related to energy and how to acquire more of it. We use the word 'energy' in our vocabulary every day, and yet when the average person is faced with the question of what energy actually is, they often become befuddled.

The reason why we hesitate to talk in detail about energy may be because it's mostly invisible to the naked eye—but so are many of the best things in life, such as love, time, music, and virtues.

There once was a time when many thought the world was flat. Progress has come in medicine as much as in geography. Before 1850, a man could be thrown into the insane asylum for suggesting that there were such things as bacteria, viruses, and microorganisms that caused sickness and disease. Surgeons once practiced multiple surgeries without washing their hands in between patients. Once the microscope was invented, microorganisms could be seen, the germ theory was developed and attitudes changed. A similar paradigm shift is happening in the field of medicine today, as science is able to show the effectiveness of energy healing. Even Western medicine currently uses energy in many of their techniques including MRI, ultrasound, laser surgery, thermography, and radiation.

Energy doesn't just exist in the world, but is abundant in the human body. Scientists are now proving through quantum physics that *everything* is energy, and scientific equipment can now measure energy very clearly. We are literally swimming in an ocean of energy and vibration. If you take the most solid material, whether it is a piece of heavy oak furniture, sheet metal, or a huge rock, it will prove not to be solid at all.

As Albert Einstein once stated: 'Concerning matter, we have been all wrong. What we have called matter is energy, whose vibration has been so lowered as to be perceptible to the senses. There is no matter.'

By simply breaking down the meaning behind the words 'energy healing,' one can better understand that it is not some dangerous form of New Age medicine.

Energy is everything and everywhere, and to manipulate it for healing purposes is a good thing that follows the laws of nature.

However, my patient did have a right to be concerned about the principles of healing through energy. This is because the intentions and expertise of the energy healer will have a dramatic impact on the success of a treatment. For instance, a medical doctor may unnecessarily prescribe harmful medications or surgery to unsuspecting patrons simply to increase their income. Receiving energy healing from a qualified practitioner is really no different. I feel it's always important to find a health care provider who not only possesses expertise but also good intentions towards their patients.

Chapter Seven:
Emotions and Healing

Facing the Fiend

When I studied medical qigong in California, my teacher emphasized how important emotions are to our health. He taught us that when we worked with patients, deep-seated emotional traumas and memories could surface. This was normal and an indicator of progress, because past emotional energies could get stuck in a person's physical tissues and affect their physical, mental, and emotional health. Just like a psychotherapist uses talk therapy to bring up a patient's old traumas and memories, the qigong therapist uses hands-on energetic techniques to encourage the release of suppressed emotions.

A cheerful heart is good medicine,
but a crushed spirit dryeth up the bones.

Proverbs 17:22

My teacher shared his experiences of what happened during this emotional 'purging' process in some of his patients. At the time I found these stories hard to believe. Although I trusted my teacher to speak the truth, this was the sort of thing I had to see for myself to fully believe.

Six months later, I had an unusual experience of my own. My patient Barbara was a pleasant woman of about forty-five years. She had been bringing in her two kids for acupuncture and qigong sessions for several months. After seeing how the medical qigong treatments relieved her son's persistent anxiety, Barbara decided to try it for her-self.

Barbara presented with anxiety and severe heart palpitations in her chest. She hinted at some childhood emotional stress, so I probed if there had been any abuse in her childhood. She didn't say that she had experienced physical or sexual abuse, but she painted a picture of her father as a man with deviant sexual behaviors. I asked her for specific memories of her childhood and her father. When she said she had no memories of her life before age seven, I warned her that intense emotional releases might happen during the treatment as memories surfaced. She understood. 'Do what you have to do, I just want it all out!'

I stood by the table as she lay quietly and comfortably on her back for her first medical qigong session. I did my standard 'hookup' with a short meditation and prayer calling on Jesus for protection, light, and love. Whenever I do this, I feel the energy in the room shift and become aware of Jesus' presence inside me. This feels energizing and soothing, and it gives me reassurance as I delve energetically into my patient's body.

I energized her tissues, then purged turbid energies from her body. As I worked on her lungs, her body contorted and her neck turned to one side. Normally, my eyes are in a soft gaze and sometimes closed in an almost meditative state. When her body started contorting, however, my eyes were wide open, like I was watching a thrilling movie. In fact, the one that comes to mind is The Exorcist. Whatever entity I was pulling out of her body, it was not a healthy one.

I performed a series of weekly sessions on Barbara, and during each treatment her body contorted into various positions.

In medical qigong, there are three main things we do during a session. We purge any unhealthy energies, which often are emotional in nature, relating to previous events and traumas in a person's life. We infuse the body with energy in areas that are deficient. Then we balance and regulate their energy in order to bring about some equilibrium. Most of Barbara's writhing and contorting occurred while I purged her body.

Concerned, I consulted with my teacher after one of Barbara's intense sessions, and he assured me that it was important to continue the purging process. Barbara herself was understanding and comfortable with the process and urged me to continue.

During the course of these treatments, I gave Barbara specific qigong breathing exercises and meditations to perform each night to help her bring up buried memories and emotions. If Barbara could reconnect with some of those childhood memories, she could reclaim that aspect of her soul and begin to truly heal. She practiced them regularly.

One night, while practicing some of the meditations, Barbara felt her body being taken over by some unknown force. She had what she called 'nightmare meditations' that lasted about an hour almost every night. She felt her body being contorted in all directions as she relived bodily memories of abuse and torment as a very young child. She said that each night the meditations progressed in age, starting at age two and the last being at age six. She never saw the face of the perpetrator; she simply felt the experiences.

With each session I went deeper, peeling layers of toxic, turbid energy from her body. After the fourth session, things escalated. Barbara stated that all she saw was darkness and she felt deep despair. This was followed by the sensation that someone was choking her and she could not breathe. Startled, I tried not to let fear enter my heart. I stayed calm and centered and trusted in the power of the Holy Spirit working through me.

I continued purging, and I simultaneously brought down white light and emitted it into her body. Her body contorted into an implausible position, with her neck bent to one side as if in a brace and her back arched upward off of the table. While I couldn't fathom what was holding her body in this posture, I kept going with the treatment. She then spoke to me in a barely perceived gasp, saying she felt as if she was being choked and could hardly breathe. I knew I couldn't stop, so I continued working even more fervently as her body contorted in varying positions and her breathing seemed labored.

After about five to ten more minutes of this work, her writhing body collapsed as if someone had been holding her up off the table a few inches then thrown her down in disgust.

At this stage, I had not awakened my gift of sight. Although many of my colleagues could see this sort of phenomena energetically, I could not. I could only go by what I saw from a physical perspective. I had the impression that someone or something, apparently fed up with the healing work, just tossed her onto the table and left for good.

Barbara just lay motionless on the table for several minutes as if she had been through a physical battle, fatigued but relieved and able to breathe normally again.

Why would anyone want to have medical qigong done, considering how much emotional and physical pain it can involve? Remember, the recipients of Jesus' healings often went into convulsions too, writhing in pain, screaming, or crying. I liken it to having a thorn stuck in your flesh. You could leave the thorn in and risk infection and a buildup of scar tissue around the wound. Or you could deal with the momentary pain as the doctor makes a small incision and pulls out the thorn. Both scenarios cause discomfort, but the latter is quicker to deal with and gets to the root of the issue, creating a true healing.

In most depictions of exorcisms, the inflicted go through a similar transition in which they kick, scream, writhe in pain, make ungodly sounds, and contort their bodies in bizarre positions as the evil spirits are taken out of them. I am not claiming to have performed an exorcism, but I do trust that some sort of unhealthy energy was taken out of Barbara's body that day.

When a patient seeks my assistance in healing a long lasting illness, be it mental or physical, I can often feel deep-seated emotions and memories in the body's tissues. With my patient's permission, I try to release these turbid energies to initiate true healing. During this process, a patient can experience an array of sensations and phenomena, some of which may or may not be pleasant. However, if the patient is ready and willing to let these energies go, the brief period of trauma can be well worth the trouble. This sort of healing reaction can create permanent relief from the symptoms that have haunted them for decades. But dramatic occurrences such as Barbara's are rare in my clinic. Most patients relax peacefully on the table during the session and often fall asleep.

For true healing to take place in many diseases, it is essential to get at the root of the problem, which I believe is often emotional or spiritual in nature. Then you can often witness extraordinary differences in a person's overall well-being.

Years later, Barbara became a healer herself. Now she uses medical qigong to help others. She wrote this letter to me some time after our work together:

Ted,

From the first treatment I just knew that the medical qigong treatments you gave me were something I needed to do and would finally lead to the healing I had sought most of my life. You led my mind to a place I'd never before known existed, a place of beauty. After the first session I felt like a fire was put out that I hadn't known was raging. I would leave each session feeling physically weak, depleted, and barely able to move—however, emotionally I felt such peace and stability. I have lost almost all the anger that was a constant companion. Resentment is now nearly non-existent and most of the fears that I carried are almost all gone.

Any fears that do exist soon disappear when I call upon the Holy Spirit as I feel an incredibly peaceful blanket of serenity pour over me.

Ted, meeting you and being a beneficiary of your medical qigong healing changed my life completely. My profound gratitude for your gift is part of my soul.

Barbara

Emotions as Energy

A fool gives full vent to his spirit, but a wise man quietly holds it back. Proverbs 29:11

We all know that emotions are a natural way for humans to express their feelings. However, as much as we are aware that emotions are real, they cannot be seen by the naked eye, nor can they be measured with any medical or scientific instrument. They are, by definition, simply states of consciousness, manifestations of energy within our bodies that we either internalize or express outwardly.

All people feel and express various emotions throughout their lifetimes. Emotions can be helpful at times and serve a great purpose.

For example, if someone threatens you, anger can help push him or her away and help you establish healthy boundaries with people. Sometimes a bit of fear can motivate you to attain higher goals. A friend told me how he was camping in the woods one time and a bear attacked his camp. In a state of fear, my friend scurried up a tree, escaping the danger. Later that evening, he tried several times to replicate the tree scaling. Minus the fear and a strong dose of adrenaline, he couldn't do it.

Fear and anger fall into the category of 'negative' emotions, while joy, love, humility, peace, compassion, and trust are classified as 'positive' emotions or virtues. Most of us dislike the negative emotions of sadness, fear, anger, rage, worry, guilt, shame, and anxiety. However, these emotions are also a natural part of our day-to-day lives. In this book I will simply refer to 'negative' emotions as emotions and 'positive' emotions as virtues.

Although it's natural to feel and express emotions, they are mostly an annoyance to our daily lives, and we often try to avoid or suppress them. They can affect our moods, relationships, jobs, and health, and even our spiritual state. Suppressed sadness can turn to depression, an excess of anger can create high blood pressure, too much fear and worry can lead to chronic anxiety, and those states can cripple us. Uncontrolled rage can lead to violence with others, which can cause injury, jail time, or death.

In the Bible, many times we are encouraged to avoid unhealthy emotions and breed virtue. Jesus recognizes that emotions like fear and anger are innate to experience on this earthly realm, but he urges us to learn to temper them.

'In your anger do not sin: Do not let the sun go down while you are still angry, and do not give the devil a foothold. Get rid of all bitterness, rage and anger, brawling and slander, along with every form of malice' (Ephesians 4:26-31).

So, should we throw a person in jail for having irritable bowel syndrome or give someone with arthritis the electric chair? Of course not! Understanding physical illness and offering compassion to those in need is a natural extension of our Christian faith. I believe that we should offer the same understanding to those who sometimes allow their emotions to get the better of them. Instead of casting someone off due to an emotional issue like anger, we could attempt to better understand their situation and heal them.

As Christians we are not taught to toss someone into a cell for the rest of their lives or to send them to the electric chair. We are meant to help others and attempt to understand emotional diseases. Jesus said, when questioned why he was eating and drinking with the tax collectors and the sinners, 'It is not those who are healthy who need a physician, but those who are sick. I didn't come to call the righteous, but sinners' (Mark 2:17).

I find it fascinating how often my patients notice the correlation between their emotions and their health. However, instead of 'emotion' I hear the word 'stress.' Patients will go on at length about their symptoms and then finish with, 'I think it's just stress.' Some patients describe their symptoms and then say, 'My doctor said that it's due to stress.' The stress referred to in these instances is not usually physical stress but the emotional and mental stress created from job and family issues.

How do we respond to stressful events? Since emotions arise from within, how can we blame them on events that occur externally? Why is it that two people can react to the exact same life event so differently?

Once, while I was teaching medical qigong, I pulled two students aside and politely gave them some constructive criticism in regards to the treatment protocol that we were practicing. I delivered the same words, to two different people, at the same time. Two days later, both students approached me separately about my advice. However, each had a different perception of what I'd said, and their emotional responses differed. One student, pleasant and upbeat in nature, thanked me for the advice. She hadn't realized her mistakes, but once she did, she made some immediate corrections and noticed fantastic results. She was grateful for my words and suggestions. I told her that it was my pleasure to help and we moved on.

The other student accused me of attacking her and 'cussing her out' in front of everyone. I told her in a calm voice, 'Debbie, I never cursed at you. I never even raised my voice.' She used some profanities toward me, cried, and then ran out the door to her car. I followed her out and we talked it over for a few minutes. Once she realized that I truly didn't intend anything personal toward her, she calmed down and apologized. She then admitted that her reaction was due to an accumulation of recent personal issues rather than my words or actions.

Our emotional responses to events are based on how our minds perceive each situation, which is based on how our thought processes have been molded. We often blame other people for our reactions and our emotions, but we have a choice on how we respond to stressful situations and difficult people. For example, if two siblings lose a beloved parent to cancer, one could react with depression and despair. The other might express an understanding that their parent is free of suffering and feel confident that they now rest in a much better place.

Emotions contain great power, and suppressing them requires an enormous amount of energy. Just imagine a young child who falls and scrapes her knee, trying to suppress her instinct to cry. No matter how much you hold the child, kiss her wound, comfort her, and tell her that everything is okay, that avalanche of emotions has already started and there's no stopping it.

As we get older, however, we learn that it's not appropriate to cry in public or to unleash our anger on co-workers in the workplace. We suppress our emotions and hold them inside, or we let them out later while complaining to our friends, family, or even our pets. This is a great form of therapy for us, but not so enjoyable for our friends and family.

The Spirit of Emotions

But the fruit of the Spirit is love, joy, peace, patience, kindness, goodness, faithfulness, gentleness, self-control; against such things there is no law. Galatians 5:22

As I have become more cognizant of how emotions affect my health, I try to be more mindful of my own mental state. When I find myself complaining about purely trivial matters, I try to catch myself. First I remind myself that everything is trivial. Then I do my best to let go of the needless emotional reaction. Often I recall how Jesus responded to extremely challenging life events.

Jesus had hundreds, likely thousands, of sick people seeking his help. Jesus was often presented with those who were mentally ill, lepers, prostitutes, paraplegics, and even those, like Lazarus, who were already deceased! Instead of reacting with disgust, irritability, or indifference, time and time again Jesus responded with love, compassion, trust, and patience.

When Jesus fasted for forty days and forty nights while he meditated and prayed in the desert seeking divine guidance, he displayed fortitude, perseverance, strength, and faith.

When his own disciples turned on him during his last hours, he responded with forgiveness, loyalty, and understanding. The common man might react with rage, bitterness, and revenge. Even though Jesus had the power to escape or even turn back his murderers in his last hours, he reacted with fearlessness, acceptance, and humility.

I now view my emotions in a similar light as my transgressions. They are a normal part of my life. I am best served to express awareness, not guilt, and mindfulness, not shame as these emotions arise. Emotions are the way in which we express ourselves in this world, and they can allow us to learn great lessons throughout life. It is healthy to feel, express, and then let go of emotions, and we are best served to teach our children not to deny them.

Personally, I want to establish a healthy relationship with myself as well as my family, friends, co-workers, and mostly with God. I've found that by controlling my emotional reactions to stressful situations by cultivating virtue in my heart and mind, I can enhance these relationships. I believe that when virtues flourish, there is little chance for negative thoughts and emotions to ripen.

In my early life I was a walking time bomb of emotions. I had issues with anger, worry, and fear, and above all, social anxiety. I can still remember being laughed off the podium during an oral presentation in college as my knees shook and my voice evaporated into a whisper.

As I crumbled in front of my peers in embarrassment, my teacher sat comfortably in the back of the room, repeating over and over, 'Ted, just relax!' Easy for her to say!

The reality is that I had no idea how to deal with my emotions. I usually let them control me and dictate how I responded to life situations. When I began studying and practicing Traditional Chinese Medicine (TCM), I saw how intimately emotions were viewed and how they affected the body. TCM offered many specific tools to regulate and balance emotions and create better health. This was so enlightening for me because I had always felt like my emotions were in control of me. I used to hide from or suppress them, which only made matters worse.

The Desert Fathers and Mothers, who were some of the earliest Christian ascetics, also noticed the great importance of regulating the emotions. Starting around the third century, these monks and nuns escaped to the deserts of Egypt for long periods of meditation in quest for enlightenment.

Like their counterparts from the Far East, they took steps toward emotional self-control, as they knew disproportionate anger, fear, or sadness would be an impediment to their spiritual progress.

One of my personal favorite meditations that I learned from my qigong teacher is an emotional releasing exercise. First I inhale while visualizing a specific virtue into the tissues of my body. I then exhale and release the negative emotions associated with that tissue or organ. I notice the many instances in the Bible where Jesus encourages us to exude virtue and temper emotions of anger, anxiety, worry, and fear. I believe that anyone who seeks peace, happiness, and health will prosper if they practice these teachings.

Spiritual Exercise: Emotional Cleansing

Sound therapy has been used by civilizations for centuries. The Daoists have used healing sound therapy in medical qigong to treat a range of diseases. The following breathing exercise benefits the heart, releases excess emotions, and resolves insomnia, anxiety, and excess heat in the body.

Sit comfortably in a chair or meditation pillow with your spine straight and arms relaxed.

Focus on breathing softly in and out through the nose for two minutes.

Begin visualizing red light entering the heart with each inhalation.

Upon each exhalation, make the HA sound as you breathe out through your mouth

Red light tonifies, or increases energy in the heart. Meanwhile, the HA sound purges stagnation from the heart.

Continue for five to ten minutes. For insomnia, you may practice while lying in bed and continue until you fall asleep.

Chapter Eight:
A Catholic Monk Goes East

Other Do Great Works

My innate childhood desire to understand Jesus' miraculous healing abilities was stymied by my early Christian teachers. I was taught to disregard Biblical inspiration such as 'Others will do greater works than I' (John 14:12) and 'You can move mountains' (Mark 11:23) and 'Anything is possible' (Mark 9:23) and 'Seek and you shall find.' (Matthew 7:7)

As I delved deeper into my studies of qigong and Eastern philosophy, I learned of legendary men who attained miraculous healing abilities much the same as Jesus Christ. These evolved beings were referred to as qigong masters.

Others will do greater works than I.

John 14:12

Immediately I wanted to learn as much as I could about these fascinating individuals.

Qigong masters have a long history in China. Much like Jesus, many were shunned, imprisoned, and even killed for demonstrating these supernatural feats, even though they were performed with the good intention to heal others.

Before the Cultural Revolution in China, qigong was associated with religion. The Communist party forbade its practice at all levels. For many years, the techniques of qigong, including the special powers one may attain from practicing the art, were kept secret. Since many people who were caught practicing qigong were punished or killed, the information stayed clandestine within martial arts sects and families. However, after the Cultural Revolution, the ban on qigong was lifted and a resurgence in this wonderful healing art developed. Today, millions of Chinese flock to the parks to practice qigong and taiji exercises every morning at dawn.

One such gathering place is Bamboo Park, where qigong Master Shr (pronounced 'Sure') teaches his students. Westerners became familiar with Master Shr following the well-received PBS documentary on qi by Bill Moyers in the 1990s. In the documentary, Master Shr demonstrates incredible feats of power simply by emitting qi from his hands like a current from an electric outlet. Many of his martial arts students attempt to attack him and take him down, but the humble and seemingly quiet Master Shr subtly but effectively tosses them to the ground. He comes across like a true Jedi Master from the Star Wars movies, which, interestingly, were inspired by Daoist traditions. The 'Force' symbolizes the Daoist principle of qi and the Hindu equivalent, prana. Director Gary Kurtz reveals that the popular phrase 'May the Force be with you' purposely mimics the common Christian salutation, 'May the Lord be with you.'

Another well-known qigong master from the East, John Chang, displays his abilities in the 1970s documentary *Ring of Fire*. In this film, Master Chang emits energy from his hands so hot that he set a pile of paper on fire in seconds. The book *Magus of Java* details Master Chang's life story and how he learned to cultivate such substantial amounts of energy by practicing meditation and qigong exercises. In addition to demonstrating qi emissions through the needles of his acupuncture patients to heal them, Master Chang also possesses abilities such as telekinesis, pyrokinesis, levitation, telepathy, electrogenesis, and remote viewing.

Yet another qigong master, Master Zhou (pronounced 'Joe'), was featured on the popular television show *That's Incredible*, demonstrating superhuman feats he attained from decades-long practice of qigong and meditation. The episode shows how Master Zhou uses qi emitted from his body to help his patients heal from a wide array of serious medical conditions. In one instance, a heat gun measures Master

Zhou's hands and verifies that the healer can emit temperatures from his palms hot enough to boil water.

One of my personal qigong students, a medical doctor named George Tenedios, went to see Master Zhou for a treatment in California. He verified that he felt extraordinary heat from Master Zhou's hands during the session and had bountiful amounts of energy and vitality in the days afterward.

While I was in India learning more about yoga, meditation, and their deep healing tradition, I discovered more about the many saints and holy persons that demonstrated feats similar to Jesus Christ's. These men are called yogis and have perfected the art and science of yoga.

One of the best-known yogis from India was Paramahansa Yogananda. His bestselling book, *Autobiography of a Yogi*, introduced Westerners to the principles of yoga and meditation back in the 1920s. Yogananda details accounts of miraculous feats by himself and some of his guru teachers. In the book, he also provides a scientific explanation for how humans can perform miraculous works, which is detailed in chapter fourteen.

The well-known Sathya Sai Baba of India was documented to have healed many diseases, levitated, and even raised the dead. He possessed the gift of clairvoyance and the ability to materialize objects at will. He passed away in 2011, but many witnessed and documented his superhuman abilities, including Howard Murphet, who wrote the book *Man of Miracles.*

In Japan, Dr. Mikao Usui, a Buddhist priest, sought the method in which Jesus and the Buddha were able to heal with the laying on of their hands. After immersing himself in a prolonged period of deep meditation, he conceived a hands-on energy healing system called reiki. Reiki is comparable to medical qigong in that the therapist channels energy into the patient by the laying on of hands. The training required to become certified in medical qigong is vastly more extensive than for reiki. I usually explain that reiki is a simplified version of medical qigong. Reiki's popularity as an effective, low-cost treatment of diseases has spread across the world.

Many Catholic nuns have used reiki in hospitals and medical centers to help those suffering from various ailments. Unfortunately, the U.S. Catholic bishops forbade the practice of reiki within the Church, claiming it was not medically or scientifically valid and incompatible with Christianity. How ironic that this same mindset two thousand years ago led to the murder of a man who *created* Christianity! I wonder how many double-blind studies proving reiki's safety and efficacy would be sufficient to persuade these bishops.

The Buddha is also known to have abilities such as reading a person's thoughts, making himself invisible, purifying dirty water, parting the waters, making himself big or small, and moving through mountains. He allegedly attained his gifts through periods of deep meditation and an ascetic lifestyle.

Learning about these masters from the East thrilled me. It renewed my interest in Jesus' healing ministry and answered many of the questions I had when I was a child. It also awakened my inherent Christian belief that we all occupy the spirit of God and that anything is possible in this world.

Interfaith Encounter

Although I was extracting knowledge from Eastern religions to enhance my understanding of Christ, I still felt an emptiness inside. As far as I knew, Catholicism didn't incorporate Eastern teachings in its catechism, nor did the Church generally approve of Eastern forms of healing and energy work. It seemed to denounce these practices altogether. I was confused. How could there be such a lack of acceptance when I saw so many correlations between the way Jesus and the Eastern healers lived their lives? I wondered if I was going against my Catholic upbringing by delving into Eastern medicine so fervently, but I never felt guilt or remorse. I was certain that what I was doing enhanced, not threatened, my relationship with and understanding of Christ.

At the time, seeing a devout Catholic at an Eastern medicine seminar or conference would have been like seeing a mouse at a cat convention. It just didn't happen. This all changed when I visited the National Qigong Association's (NQA) yearly conference in Baltimore, Maryland.

It was the summer of 2009. I was juggling two private practices in Gettysburg, Pennsylvania and Bethesda, Maryland while also teaching medical qigong certification courses at my center in Gettysburg and in Montreal, Canada where I assisted my teacher. My teacher, Dr. Bernard Shannon, gave a lecture at the NQA conference that July. Among the small audience was a peculiar gentleman in his early sixties who caught my attention.

After the session, my teacher introduced us. 'Ted, this is Brother Bernard Seif, he's a Catholic monk.'

A significant member from the Catholic Church community at a qigong conference! I felt relief and joy to meet a Catholic monk, but I was also intensely curious. For all the years that I had studied qigong and Chinese medicine, I'd never met anyone within any order of the Catholic Church at any course or seminar. At last I knew I was not alone in this healing journey.

I had the great pleasure of speaking to Brother Seif as he enlightened me about others within the Church who had inspired *him* to learn more about meditation and Eastern spiritual practices.

Brother Seif told me about the deep history of meditation and healing within the Catholic Church, and about his personal travels to China to learn medical qigong and incorporate it into his practice. He had made many efforts to bridge the gap between Christianity and Eastern religions. 'I've spent my life trying to encourage mutual respect among religions, and this experience, where we both remained faithful to our spiritual traditions yet shared life-giving practices, was life-giving for me also. It is the sort of attitude that can end war, I believe.'

When I asked Brother Seif about his experiences using qigong, he shared this story: 'I remember one woman in her eighties who had several tumors on some vital organs. She told me she was ready to die, but came to me for a few medical qigong treatments and the tumors went away! Of course I consistently referred her back to her oncologist and encouraged her cooperation with him. Then she came back, and I would just see her periodically for a tune up, and while I was doing some qigong on her, she hollered out, "Thank you Jesus—and I'm Jewish!" It was so funny and delightful! She's still living today and this was years ago.'

Brother Seif talked about his early years in training as a monk in a Catholic monastery. In between long periods of silence and meditation, he would read in the small library, and there he discovered books by Thomas Merton. Merton was also a Catholic monk who was a steadfast advocate of interfaith understanding, promoting interchanges with key spiritual figures within the Asian community, including the Dalai Lama, and authoring many books on Daoist and Zen philosophy. Merton and his works became inspiration for many Catholics, including Brother Seif.

As Brother Seif's passion for Eastern teachings grew, he visited Asia many times and had opportunities to study and train with qigong masters in China. Listening to him speak about his qigong training, I began to draw strong correlations with my own education. He shared another story about his training in the qigong hospitals in Beijing with the well-known medical qigong doctor, Feng Lida.

'Just being in that qi field and seeing so many doctors working in a room together on patients with different ailments was so helpful. Sometimes you'd have over thirty doctors in one room doing medical qigong on people. But Feng Lida was the one I remember the most. We would have classes in the afternoon and practice the various qigong movements as well. In the evenings, the staff would come to our hotel rooms and treat us with medical qigong to help us experience what patients experience.

'The teachers would talk a lot about cleansing and purging first, followed by transmitting qi to the patient. My teachers would talk a lot about the two models of medical qigong treatment. So, for example, a lot them would think of the lower dantian as a battery, and they would go outside and absorb the qi in the very early morning and then run this internal battery all day while treating patients. Then some others, I think they would be the minority, would use the energy of the Divine and simply act as a conduit. This is how I generally do it when I treat patients.

'One of my teachers said, "If you give a treatment well, you get a treatment." This is because the qi flows through you as it moves to the patient. Also, as you cleanse the qi field of the patient, you can also cleanse yourself. Many people are afraid of being infected, so to speak, by the contaminated qi of the patient. I am prudent when treating people but am not overly concerned about that. I love Ken Cohen's teaching that there is no such thing as evil or contaminated qi. All true qi is healthy. Sometimes it gets stagnant and needs to be recycled, like compost, however.'

Meeting with Brother Seif was illuminating. What a relief: there were Catholics who followed the same path as I. Brother Seif told me that many others within the Catholic Church have integrated Eastern philosophies and healing techniques into their work. For example, as previously stated, many nuns use reiki on patients in the hospitals as they see this work as a natural extension of Christ's healing ministry. This meeting inspired me to look even further for evidence of other Christians who have used Eastern medicine and performed miraculous healings.

A Modern Mystic: Sister Chris

With the excitement of meeting Brother Seif fresh on my mind, I wanted to share this story with someone else. Not even a week later, I met with a good friend and colleague, Nancy Hill, for a massage at the Gettysburg Holistic Health Center. Nancy is a gifted healer who practices massage, medical qigong, and reflexology and is an expert with essential oils.

During the session I mentioned how I met a Catholic monk who practiced energy healing like us. As she noticed my excitement, she quickly interjected, 'You should talk to Sister Chris!'

Nancy informed me of a Catholic nun named Christine, going by 'Sister Chris,' who practiced reiki healing. Nancy had met her through a mutual friend and told me that she lived in New Jersey. That night I wrote a formal email to Sister Chris requesting a possible visit to interview her. She replied back the next day, expressing delight in the idea of my book and happily agreeing to be interviewed.

Mind you, although I was raised Catholic, my only previous knowledge of Catholic nuns came from stories that my older sisters and other family members shared with me over the years. I hadn't gone to Catholic school as a kid and there weren't any active nuns at St. Catherine's Church in Leeds, Massachusetts, where I grew up. Many of the stories I heard about nuns in the Church involved my family's experiences in Catholic school, since nuns were the primary teachers.

I was shocked to learn that many nuns physically and verbally abused my friends and family during their years in Catholic school. Back then teachers in all schools had much more authority and power. Nuns also had the difficult challenge of teaching classes of over thirty students by themselves. It was essential that they displayed a stern disposition early and often to maintain order in the classroom.

Although I had heard many horror stories about nuns, I was certain that most were very kind and compassionate in nature. Such was the case with Sister Chris, as I felt nothing but positive energy in our many email exchanges. Although her replies were pleasant, they were succinct, and we did not speak on the phone at all prior to our meeting.

All I had was an address in New Jersey. I truly had no idea what her home would be like. My knowledge of the daily life of a nun was minimal. When I think of them, I picture the black and white habit and veil that is the most common attire. But what would Sister Chris be wearing, and where did she live? I wasn't sure if she lived at or near a church or possibly in a convent with other nuns. I was aware that things have changed dramatically for nuns in the Catholic Church over the years. However, I was still unaware of the details and curious as to what I would experience. Either way, I was eager to meet Sister Chris and to find out more about her life and how she became interested in energy healing.

As I drove into the condominium complex where Sister Chris lived, I started to relax a bit more. Knowing that she likely lived alone in a typical American home, I figured on an informal experience. She opened the door to her apartment, dressed casually, and with a smile as she welcomed me inside. If I hadn't known she was a nun I would have never guessed. She appeared no different than any other woman in her late fifties.

When we sat down, one of the first things she shared with me was the difference between nuns and sisters. She explained that nuns are members of enclosed religious orders and take solemn religious vows, through which they renounce many of the material aspects of life. They usually live contemplative lives in a convent or monastery and spend many an hour in meditation. Sisters have much simpler vows, which include being allowed to inherit property. Sisters live, pray, and minister within the world and often serve the poor, needy, and ill. She likened it to the comparison between a Catholic monk and priest. However, the terms 'sister' and 'nun' are often used interchangeably, and for the sake of this writing I will often refer to both simply as nuns.

Sister Chris then took me through a typical day in her life. She begins with some prayer followed by physical exercise. Then she sees clients at her home, using various energy healing techniques and massage therapy.

What impressed me right away about Sister Chris was her positive outlook, which I often have noticed in highly evolved beings. When asked about her early life, she told me how her father left her when she was only four years old and her mother was in a mental hospital. I was shocked because she preceded this statement with, 'I happened to be a very fortunate person when I was young.' She then explained how, after her father left, she had several profound experiences, which helped her develop a strong relationship with God. This inspired a spiritual path and set the tone for her current life.

She led me more through her early years and expounded on how she became interested in the healings arts. Like myself, she started her journey practicing bodywork on others in the form of massage therapy. One of her teachers practiced reiki healing and inspired her along the same path. Sister Chris eventually became certified as a reiki master and instructor. For years she taught others how to perform reiki healing, which she enjoyed very much. At the time practicing reiki was common for many nuns within the Catholic Church. They found this to be natural extension of their Christian faith and acknowledgement of the fact that Jesus encouraged his disciples to promote and practice hands on healing.

She detailed how the Catholic bishops expressed discouragement towards the use of reiki. They took notice how many nuns used reiki in hospitals and medical clinics to alleviate pain and suffering to those in need. They discussed the matter and eventually deemed reiki as superstitious and incompatible with Christianity. Then they advised Catholics not to provide or support this practice.

I specifically asked Sister Chris if she felt that Jesus had any connections with Eastern healing traditions. Sister Chris told me that she felt Eastern forms of energy healing such as reiki were quite similar in nature to how Jesus healed. She also shared my belief that Jesus did indeed travel to India to teach and learn during the lost years.

Fortunately for Sister Chris, she practiced another Asian healing system called Jin Shin Jyutsu. Similar to reiki in having Japanese roots, Jin Shin Jyutsu is a form of bodywork like acupressure. Being well versed in acupressure therapy, where various acupuncture points are stimulated to promote qi flow within the body, I understood the concepts behind Jin Shin Jyutsu quite well.

Sister Chris told me that she felt she was able to initiate similar, if not greater, healing results with Jin Shin Jyutsu as with reiki. So when the bishops urged Catholic nuns to stop using reiki to heal, Sister Chris simply transitioned to using Jin Shin Jyutsu and massage only, to avoid any potential repercussion within the Church.

Yet at the same time she was able to continue to use energy healing techniques to help her clients.

Currently, reiki studies are being conducted at the National Center for Complementary and Alternative Therapies on the NIH campus in Bethesda, Maryland. The early results are promising and I am confident that science will soon recognize reiki as a safe and effective therapy. Once the doubt and skepticism regarding reiki is extinguished, I'm hopeful the Catholic Church might change its stance.

Our meeting concluded with Sister Chris offering to treat me with Jin Shin Jyutsu. I was delighted to receive a treatment from her and happily accepted the offer. I lay on the massage table as she began her work. I remember laying there thinking how lucky I was for so many reasons. First, to receive a wonderful healing session from a talented healer. But also to be discovering so much about how many Christians at all levels of the Church are practicing energy healing techniques just as I feel Jesus did two thousand years ago. This was just the beginning of more wonderful discoveries in my quest to connect the dots, discovering the healing Jesus.

Saints Do Greater Works

I was delighted to learn that there were hundreds of Catholics, mostly canonized saints, who had performed many of the same miraculous healing works as Jesus and even greater works indeed!

Padre Pio (1887-1968) is one of the best-known and highly documented holy persons within the Catholic Church to have performed miracles. In addition to his many healings, he had the gifts of bilocation and clairvoyance, and he demonstrated stigmata much of his adult life. As his legend grew, the Vatican became skeptical. However, most of Padre Pio's abilities were well documented and witnessed by many. Padre Pio later became canonized as a saint within the Catholic Church. The book *Padre Pio: The Wonder Worker*, edited by Francis Mary, describes his life and gifts.

Saint Vincent Ferrer (1350-1419) was another highly respected Christian who performed hundreds of miracles and displayed supernatural abilities. The Archbishop of Florence, St. Antonius, stated that St. Vincent raised twenty-eight persons from the dead. He displayed power over evil spirits and freed over seventy possessed persons. His passion for preaching the Gospel was so strong that he apparently converted tens of thousands of non-Christians during his life. The *Acta Sanctorum* records eight hundred and seventy-three miracles by this saint, and many more went unrecorded. St. Vincent was highly revered and often compared to the twelve apostles because of his works. His life is well recorded in the book *St. Vincent Ferrer: Angel of Judgement* by Andrew Pradel.

Levitation is another common gift of holy persons, both from Christian backgrounds and in masters from the Far East. Saint Joseph Cupertino (1603-1663) was so well known for his ability to levitate during deep periods of prayer that, for more than thirty-five years, his superiors would not allow him to take part in some of the weekly processions in fear that he might disturb the congregation. The Catholic Church regards him affectionately as the patron saint of airplane passengers. His miraculous life is detailed in the movie *The Reluctant Saint* and in the book *St. Joseph Cupertino* by Angelo Pastrovicchi.

Blessed Alexandrina da Costa (1904-1955) led a humble life with much suffering and pain as a Christian mystic. Her strong faith allowed her to be blessed by direct communion with Jesus Christ. After this experience, she went without food and water for her thirteen final years, living only on the energy of the Holy Spirit that burned strong in her. When suspicion arose about her claimed fast, strict supervision was forced on her. The medical professionals confirmed and certified the fast.

These are just a few examples from hundreds of Christian saints who have performed miraculous healings, displayed psychic gifts, bilocated, raised the dead, levitated, and accomplished other supernatural phenomena. Miracle workers and healers come in different forms and are exemplified within all the major religions of the world.

These miracle workers, although vastly different in many ways, also have poignant similarities.

They all demonstrate a virtuous and holy lifestyle and do not seek fame or fortune. Although some are born with natural psychic and spiritual gifts, most have developed or maintained their abilities through disciplined meditative practices such as qigong, yoga, breathing exercises, prayer, mantra, and meditation.

Brother Seif said that, unfortunately, much of this hidden mystical knowledge 'never reaches the pews.' In other words, many Catholics are privy to this knowledge, but many others are denied these empowering teachings. There are seven holy sacraments within the Catholic Church. Brother Seif believes that there should be an eighth sacrament, the promotion of healing within the Church, since this was Jesus' main ministry. I support Brother Seif's position and hope that this book helps spread the inspiration.

Chapter Nine:
Love, the Greatest Commandment

Amma and Forgiveness

In 2004, I experienced another enlightening moment that altered the way I viewed sin and the Ten Commandments. While I was in California for one of my medical qigong trainings, I learned from a friend that Amma, a Hindu spiritual guru from India, was touring the United States. Affectionately known as 'the Hugging Saint,' she was holding a retreat nearby in San Francisco.

Had this invitation been presented to me ten years prior, I would have declined, because I thought this type of gathering conflicted with my Christian faith.

Dear friends, let us love one another,
for love comes from God. Everyone who
loves has been born of God and knows God.

1 John 4:7

However, I had since delved into Eastern philosophies and knew that Amma had won worldwide humanitarian awards, so I felt comfortable giving her a visit.

I liked that she didn't ask for money. She blesses hundreds of thousands of people per year and gives discourses and teachings to all who visit her, free of charge. Donations she receives are recycled back into her many humanitarian efforts.

Shunning money isn't the only similarity she had with Jesus Christ. She spreads compassion, love, and forgiveness to the crowds who seek her healing touch. She actually exemplified Jesus more than anyone I had ever met before.

A small, motherly type draped in a figure-concealing white garment, she blessed nearly a thousand visitors over several hours. Her hugs felt as if being hugged by a mother who hadn't seen her child in years.

Then she sat down on the ground with us and spoke through a translator, answering questions.

A slender woman in the audience raised her hand to ask Amma for advice. She had committed many transgressions and was weighed with guilt. What should she do?

I expected Amma to send this woman to some private tent where she would have to recite ten Gayatri mantras and fifteen Shri Krishnu Aarti prayers.

Amma simply replied with a loving smile, 'Forget about it, and do better tomorrow.'

The woman stumbled back a step, her lips parted in disbelief. Even with her head bowed in humility, her whole body looked straighter and emanated relief, like a huge burden had been lifted off her.

Wow! Could it be that easy? No need for confession or penance, no feelings of shame or guilt?

Much like the woman who asked the question, I also had a weight taken off my shoulders, and it felt good.

When I was a kid, parts of the Bible scared me—especially the one that said that if you dishonored your parents, you should be put to death (Matthew 15:4). I can still remember going to confession during my childhood, always having the 'I disobeyed my parents' sin first on my list.

So, when I saw Amma and listened to her words, it was as if a hot air balloon full of guilt, shame, and fear had been disconnected from my being, and it felt wonderful. However, a part of me felt guilty for not feeling guilty.

Months later, I was reading through the Bible, searching for verses about sin, forgiveness, and the Ten Commandments. In the Book of John (8:7), I came to a verse about Jesus in the temple that was eerily similar to the experience that I had with Amma in California. When the scribes and Pharisees brought an adulterer to Jesus, ready to punish her according to Moses' law, Jesus simply said, 'Let he who is without sin cast the first stone.' One by one, they all dropped their stones and walked away. Jesus approached the woman and said, 'I do not condemn you, so go and sin no more.'

This reminded me that Jesus was not condemning, but loving and forgiving. It didn't serve me to feel any shame or guilt for my faults. These verses directed me to be mindful of my actions and my mistakes, but also to simply dust myself off and try to do better next time. It also assured me that Amma and Jesus were not all that different in their manner and preaching.

What is Sin?

If you mention the word 'sin' to anyone raised Christian, it often invokes disgust, unworthiness, and other negative emotions. Sin is never a good thing, and must be avoided at all costs to live a holy life and avoid punishment. Many Christians associate sin with Satan, hell, condemnation, hatred, and crime.

But what is sin exactly? 'Sin' translated in Hebrew simply means 'to miss.' It doesn't mean to commit an immoral act; it means to miss or to not be present. Sin is a lack of awareness or a lack of consciousness. This is similar to Buddhist teachings of being present or Krishna's teaching of being more aware.

When Jesus speaks of sinning, he is reminding us that we missed the mark and can try again. In life, when we see someone trying hard but not hitting the target, we encourage them to try again and teach them to do better. Over and over, Jesus demonstrated this when he spent so much of his time with sinners, inspiring them to hit the mark and come closer to God. Jesus knew that the world was imperfect and we all make mistakes. Jesus came to us to guide us towards a healthier path back to God. He came to show us forgiveness, inspiration, and love, not to make us feel guilty and ashamed.

Not only is sin a natural part of our lives, but so often we learn the greatest lessons when we miss the mark. The pain and disharmony we experience from sinning often motivates us to strive for better results in the future. Again, it's all about being more conscious of our deeds and has nothing to do with punishment or condemnation. When successful people are asked how they achieve so much, they often say it was their mistakes that made them who they are today.

Simply put, I feel that sin is any act that takes you farther from God. Loving and healing actions toward ourselves, and others, bring us closer to God. God gave us the wonderful gift of free will to choose as we wish. Obviously, God wants his children to come closer to him, but I do not feel that we are being commanded or forced. We control our own destiny and fate. We create our own heaven and hell right here and right now with our thoughts, actions, and deeds.

Jesus' New Commandments

As my journey into Eastern Medicine and Eastern religions deepened over the years, I took a closer look at how each of these religions interpreted sin. Specifically, I noticed how most Eastern religions recognized the same set of laws as the Ten Commandments taught in Christianity and Judaism. Most religions state that it's not spiritually beneficial to lie, cheat, murder, steal, or hurt others.

However, the Eastern approaches to these laws are often different. Instead of commands, you tend to see beliefs, tenets, principles, and ways of life.

Also, there seems to be less focus on the negative act that we are to avoid and more emphasis on what we should strive for in our quest for enlightenment. Instead of rules with negative words like murder, adultery, theft, and coveting, they use more uplifting expressions.

The Hindu disciplines speak of celibacy, truth, nonviolence, cleanliness, and prayer. In Buddhist tenets you hear words like peace, love, right thought, right speech, and right action. One can interpret a tone of incentive and reward, rather than punishment, in the Daoist precept that reads 'When I see someone do a good deed, I will support him with joy and delight.'

Jesus presented a set of laws inspiring us to honor God and to refrain from heinous acts against our fellow beings. However, they were far different from the Commandments that Moses delivered hundreds of years before. Jesus' laws also didn't contain the uninspiring words of murder, sex, lies, cursing, or theft. Jesus spoke these commandments when his followers asked which were most important: 'You shall love the Lord your God with all your heart, and with all your soul, and with all your mind. This is the great and foremost commandment. The second is like it: You shall love your neighbor as yourself. On these two commandments depend the whole Law and the Prophets' (Matthew 22:36-40).

How brilliant to simply be encouraged to love! Jesus recognized that a world without murder, lies, cheating, stealing, sickness, and immoral acts would lead us closer to God. He recognized the power of being positive in all thoughts when trying to inspire us to higher levels of consciousness. Dark words—murder, theft, sickness, cheating, stealing, lies, adultery—can breed darkness in one's soul, and so Jesus did not use them. He simply taught us to love. Maybe he knew that if we truly focused on loving others, all of man's heinous activities would gradually cease. When darkness invades a room, simply turning on a light will make it flee. I feel Jesus knew that turning on our 'love light' would do the same thing to sin, wrongdoing, and disease.

I have interpreted a few things from these proclamations. First, in shifting to a more positive tone, it seemed that Jesus understood the spiritual progress man had made in the centuries after Moses introduced the Ten Commandments. Second, to command someone not to do something often makes a person just want to do it more. Using words like 'love' is far more powerful and inspiring than using words that remind us of R- or X-rated films. The law of love gives the spiritual aspirant a tangible tool to reach enlightenment rather than simple commands to avoid eternal damnation after life. Lastly, Jesus' overall message of love, compassion, and forgiveness coincides much more with God's gift to all humans, which is free will. How can you both command someone and give free will at the same time?

When Jesus told his disciples the day before he died, 'Little children, I am with you a little while longer. Where I am going, you cannot come. A new commandment I give to you, that you love one another, even as I have loved you, that you also love one another' (John 13:32-34), was he ushering in a new set of commands?

Lessons

Jesus' command to love above all else drastically altered the way I view God's commandments. Certainly no Christian wants to commit any of these transgressions, but there is an easier way to live righteously.

Instead of focusing on *not* killing, I now think about respecting all forms of life. Instead of thinking about *not* lying, I try my best to speak the truth when I communicate. Jesus' command of loving others really eliminates the need to tell people what not to do.

Jesus repeatedly connected our past actions with our state of health by saying that 'your sins are forgiven' when he healed the sick. By focusing on love, you heal yourself and others, because love is at the root of all healing. Happiness and good health bring us closer to God and free us from pain and suffering. From an Eastern perspective, this is the law of karma. This law states that our every word, thought, and deed has an energy and power that returns to us in some capacity. From a scientific standpoint, Newton's third law states that for every action there is an equal and opposite reaction. This is also confirmed in the Bible: Jesus often tells us that we reap what we sow. God doesn't condemn us, we condemn ourselves with our actions. It's a simple law that is confirmed by science and in most religions. We have free will to act as we please, and God is always there for us if we chose him.

These days, when I think about my actions and how they affect myself and others, I try and let go of the word 'sin' and replace it with 'karma.' The word 'sin' has gotten a bad rap, but when Jesus healed people and said, 'Your sins are forgiven,' he was simply erasing the self-imposed effects of karma on a person's body and soul.

Jesus taught us one simple rule, and that was to love. He channeled that love into his healings, and I feel that love is at the root of all healing in this world. The vibration of love carries an enormous energy and power, and Jesus spoke of love more than anything else during his many sermons.

Masters from the East also recognize love as an extraordinarily potent healing force. They observed energy centers at the area of the heart that could be regulated and nourished. The middle dantian and heart chakra are two of these energy centers that Daoists, Buddhists, and Hindu healers utilized. I learned how one can actually cultivate love by purifying the emotions and energizing these centers through meditative techniques. More discussion about these techniques and energy centers follow in later chapters.

Chapter Ten:
Bringing Meditation to the Pews

Cure-All Pill

When I visited India years ago, I stayed mostly in ashrams in Rishikesh. I went to bed early the first night, knowing I would have to get up before dawn the next day.

In the morning, I awoke to a loud, deep *dong-dong-dong*. The campus bell was calling everyone to the five am meditation. I threw on my shoes and a sweatshirt and hurried the three hundred yards from my dormitory to the temple.

Dark walls created a calm, subdued mood. Some students sat in the lotus position on the carpeted floor. For less agile participants— like myself—a bunch of pillows and even chairs were available.

Be still and know that I am God.

Psalm 46:10

I put several cushions under my butt and sat in a kind of squatting position with my lower legs tucked underneath. This was reasonably comfortable and allowed me to keep my spine straight during the meditation.

After meditation, we had a short break, then moved into the larger yoga hall next door for an hour and a half of yoga asanas. I had done yoga before, but this was like boot camp. It started gently enough, but then the teachers led us through increasingly challenging postures. After fifteen minutes, I had to admit that I just wasn't physically able to keep up, and modified the poses to make them more bearable.

I wasn't the only one struggling. Many foreign guests also grappled clumsily with the strenuous exercises, although others performed them with fluid ease.

At last it was breakfast time! By now, I was ravenous. Although the food was basic—grains, fruit, eggs, water, and tea with few seasonings or spices—I devoured the meal and it tasted wonderful.

I spent almost a month in India, immersing myself in the study and practice of yoga and meditation. Over the years, I've found meditation to be a great tool for promoting health, and I use it with many patients to enhance their treatments.

One patient named Anna came to my clinic for acupuncture treatment a few years ago. In her early forties, Anna had several health issues. Her main complaint was pain spreading throughout all the joints in her body. She was diagnosed with arthritis and fibromyalgia and had suffered for over ten years with this pain.

During her initial visit, when I tried to gather facts specific to her disease, she deluged me with details about everything else that was wrong with her life. After about fifteen minutes of this rant, I gently interjected with a question.

Since I figured she would require more than acupuncture to alleviate her problems, I said, 'Anna, what would you do if I told you that there was a pill that could help you eliminate your pain, take away your worries, relieve your depression, allow you to sleep better, *and* give you more energy. What would you say to that?'

She quickly retorted, 'There's no medication that can cure fibromyalgia!'

I told her, 'It's not a drug, it's not an herb, and it's not a vitamin...it's in your medicine cabinet at home right now. It's scientifically proven to be effective and it's totally free!'

Looking stunned, and maybe disturbed by my knowledge of her medicine cabinet's contents, she said, 'Well then, what is it?'

I replied, 'The "pill" is called meditation.'

Most of my patients quickly dismiss the notion of meditation, either because they can't believe it could possibly help them, or because they don't think they could incorporate the discipline into their lives. To my surprise, Anna didn't resist my pitch. Instead she said,

'Okay…how do I learn to do it?'

I inserted acupuncture needles at various points along her body as she lay on her back on the treatment table. I put an infrared heating lamp near her feet and dimmed the lights. Then I led her through a gentle breathing exercise to help her relax.

Acupuncture alone can induce a highly meditative state as the needles help to break all physical and emotional stagnation throughout the body. Relaxing breathing exercises can greatly enhance the healing effect of the treatment.

As I led her into the exercise, I had her focus only on her breathing and how it felt in her body. I encouraged her to bring her mind back to the breath each time it wandered off with random thoughts. I explained that every thought had energy, and every time she thought about something, this was energy dissipating from the body. If she focused within, she would turn her energy inwards, healing her own body and turning off her mental faucet. I guided her to feel the breath enter her body, imagining it saturating every cell as it energized and healed her tissues and organs.

Anna's breath became slower, deeper, and more relaxed. The tense muscles in her face and jaw seemed to melt like butter. As she drifted into a state between sleep and trance, I gently twirled the needles to stimulate the energy release at each acupuncture point where energy tends to pool.

Then I left the room quietly, and let her rest for twenty minutes.

After the treatment, Anna told me that she couldn't remember feeling so relaxed and peaceful in her whole life. Within the first three sessions combining acupuncture and breathing exercises, she noticed the promised changes. Her pain was reduced by about fifty percent, she had more energy and was sleeping better, her anxieties were less, and she had better mental clarity.

Anna embraced meditation and faithfully practiced the exercises I taught her. After six treatments, I told her she no longer required regular acupuncture if she continued to meditate.

She practiced sitting meditation, read books on meditation, took my weekly qigong meditation class, and even purchased a few CDs of other meditations. She was so thankful for learning about this practice to help her feel better. Within eight weeks, eighty percent of her pain was gone, and she felt better emotionally and physically.

Christian Meditation

Meditation is the main tool for any spiritual aspirant in Eastern religions. Whether you are a Hindu practicing yoga, a Buddhist, or a Daoist qigong healer, meditation is always the cornerstone in the quest for better health and increased consciousness. The more I studied, the more I read, and the more I practiced, the more I understood the deep, empowering aspects of meditation. Finally I had a tool that truly helped me reach for the heavens. I felt like a caveman discovering fire for the first time.

Why was I not taught meditation during my Catholic upbringing? Until I met Brother Seif, I hadn't known it was taught within the Catholic Church at all. Brother Seif had spent many hours meditating as part of his initial training, and now teaches meditation in his monastery and at a Jesuit retreat center.

There is indeed a rich tradition of meditation within Christianity and the Catholic Church.

Around 270 AD, the Christian monk Saint Paul, known as the first hermit, fled to the Theban Desert to seek solitude. Legend has it that he spent the rest of life there until he died nearly one hundred years later. During these years, Saint Paul spent much of his time fasting, praying, and meditating on the Lord. The Catholic Church honors him and to this day there's a monastery at the site of his cave.

Inspired by Saint Paul, Saint Anthony sought a Christian life of monasticism in the desert for many years. Saint Anthony soon became known as the 'Father of Monasticism' and founded the Desert Fathers who inspired hundreds of men and women to seek solitude and meditation in the depths of the deserts in Egypt. Monasticism, where one turns their senses inward, renouncing the material world and focusing purely on spiritual growth, plays an important role in many Christian churches, especially the Catholic and Orthodox traditions. The meditations of the Desert Fathers were called *hesychasm*, which is defined by the practice of silence, 'turning off' the senses and focusing inward.

In the Middle Ages, Saint John of the Cross and Saint Teresa of Avila were both strong proponents of meditation as a tool to establish union with God. They taught meditative processes that started with vocal prayer as a bridge to deeper states of meditation and silencing the mind.

Surprisingly, the teaching of meditation diminished significantly between the 17th and 20th centuries in many sects of Christianity. However, after World War II, the integral teachings of John of the Cross, Teresa Avila, and other Christian mystics were revived. At the same time, interest in Eastern meditation and mysticism blossomed. The works and teachings of Catholics like Thomas Merton, Thomas Keating, and John Main produced the 'Centering Prayer,' a form of Christian meditation widely practiced today. In addition, the meditative practices of the Lectio Divina were suggested to the Catholic community in *Dei verbum* of the Second Vatican in 1965, and Pope Benedict XVI affirmed its importance in 2005. Lectio Divina means 'Divine Reading', and is a traditional practice of scripture reading, prayer and meditation intended to promote communion with God. Pope Benedict stated that he believed this practice would bring a 'new spiritual springtime' for the Church.

I believe that some of the confusion about meditation within the Catholic Church may stem from word choice.

The quieting of the mind and practice of silence and solitude—referred to as 'meditation' in other contexts—is often called 'contemplation' in Christianity, while the word 'meditation' can refer to any combination of prayer, mantra, and contemplation.

For example, the Rosary is a set of prayers used as a tool to enter into a meditative state. However, they are often defined as being a meditation. True meditation, within Catholicism, is a process referred to as 'contemplative prayer'. The words 'prayer' and 'meditation' are often interchanged. Many of the saints mentioned earlier used active steps that included reading of the gospel, prayer, and mantra, but eventually led to a deep, quiescent state of meditation.

I believe that the confusion between prayer and meditation began in the Bible. The Old Testament contains numerous references to meditation. However, despite the evidence that Jesus practiced and taught meditation, the word 'meditation' is absent from the New Testament.

Much like the word 'prayer' has several interpretations (and misinterpretations), I believe 'meditation' has a broad definition in the Bible. When Jesus retreated to the wilderness to pray, we can assume that this involved deep meditation as well as common prayer, especially as he was also fasting. Refraining from thought as well as food is a way to purify both body and soul.

I believe that Jesus, like his followers over centuries who have meditated in his name, spent many hours of his life in deep meditation.

When Jesus instructed us how to meditate, he guided us to start with a vocal prayer. Once you open the dialogue with God, God will recompense you with his knowledge, but only when you stop the chatter and listen to his wisdom.

Jesus said, 'And when you pray, do not be like the hypocrites, for they love to pray standing in the synagogues and on the street corners to be seen by men. I tell you, they have received their reward in full. But when you pray, go into your room and close the door and pray to your Father who is unseen. Then, your Father, who sees what is done in secret, will reward you. And when you pray, do not keep on babbling like pagans, for they think they will be heard for their many words. Do not be like them, for your Father knows what you need before you ask' (Matthew 6:5-8).

This makes it unlikely that Jesus was only talking to God in the form of prayer during those forty long days and nights in the desert. It seems obvious that he sought the ultimate communion with God through meditation and by turning all his senses inward, seeking the Kingdom he said lies within each one of us.

Hesychastic practices of the Desert Fathers involve a quieting of the physical senses and a focus inward. The Hesychast interprets

Christ's words in the Gospel of Matthew to 'go into your room and close the door and pray' as meaning that one should withdraw inward.

From a healing perspective, I believe that Jesus did the same as many Eastern qigong masters and yogis, who often retreat to the wilderness for long periods of meditation to recharge. In the Bible we often see Jesus escaping to the wilderness either just before or immediately after healing the 'multitudes.' It was just before Jesus began his healing ministry in Jerusalem that he escaped to the desert for his well-known forty days and forty nights of asceticism.

The Science of Love

As a Christian studying Eastern medicine for the first time, I noticed the strong connection that all Eastern practices emphasized between meditation and good health. Meditation also nurtures one's spiritual health and relationship with God. Jesus teaches us to love one another, he teaches us to heal others, and he teaches us to be fearless and trust fully in God. Despite always hearing these commands and understanding them, I wasn't always able to fully execute them in my daily life. For example, I found it difficult to feel love and compassion to my 'neighbor' who brought me pain and anguish. Sometimes I even struggled to express love towards the people closest to me like my family and friends.

By practicing meditation regularly, I found it much easier to achieve these goals. Meditation was a tangible tool that helped me become a more moral person and a better Christian.

Studies at the University of Wisconsin-Madison show evidence that people who meditate regularly have a higher ability to express loving kindness and compassion. Using magnetic resonance imaging (MRI), researchers detected that meditation affects areas of our brain that relate to empathetic abilities. The study indicates that positive emotions—virtues—like compassion can actually be learned the same way that one learns to play tennis or play the guitar.

An even more significant study involved a group of over four thousand meditators in Washington, DC in 1993. The group approached the DC Chief of Police and explained to him that, based on previous studies, they could reduce the crime rate by twenty percent that summer. The chief initially laughed them off. The only thing that would reduce the crime rate that much in the summertime in his city, he said, would be twenty inches of snow.

During the two-month, carefully controlled study, four thousand meditators were brought into the DC area. They performed two lengthy periods of meditation per day with a particular focus on compassion and kindness. Just one week into the study, homicide, rape, and aggravated assault rates began dropping, and they continued dropping throughout the eight-week period. Amazingly, the crime rates dropped over twenty-three percent.

Interestingly, the crime rate went up immediately after the group left town. I wonder how much crime and violence would exist in this world if we all meditated for just ten minutes per day.

Many prisons are taking this a step further and teach meditation to their inmates. The results have been dramatic: lower recidivism rates; fewer rule infractions; less criminal thinking and psychological distress; decreased anxiety, depression, and anger; and an improved spiritual outlook and purposefulness.

Considering that the U.S. spends billions of tax dollars annually on corrections, teaching meditation could lead to big savings. It would also exemplify Christian forgiveness rather than revenge, healing rather than violence, and compassion rather than punishment toward wrongdoers.

Jesus offered sinners the 'reset button' when he took away our sins. Imagine a world in which we could erase someone's sins by simply teaching them to meditate.

At the same time, we would also be offering a tool to help people strengthen their compassion muscle, which is what Jesus commanded us to do above and beyond all else. I cannot think of anything more Christian than a simple technique that makes us more loving and compassionate.

The Power of Listening

A tall man in his sixties came to me for acupuncture. Not only did he suffer from pain in his lower back and legs, but he also was going through a tough divorce and struggled with life challenges. During the weekly sessions on the table, he spoke in an escalating tone about his personal issues and asked my advice. 'What do I do, Doc? What do I do?'

Between one of his breaths, I found a window to offer a suggestion. I managed to utter no more than a word or two before his next breath kicked in and he continued his verbal tirade. I chose not to force the issue and simply allowed him to vent.

Prayer is an active form of communication in which the individual speaks to God. I feel prayer is one of the most powerful tools to develop a healthy relationship with God. However, prayer differs from meditation.

If you were sitting in a room with God and you had a chance to speak to him and share your problems, or to listen to God and allow him to share his infinite wisdom, which would you chose?

Most people that I ask, after thinking about it, chose to listen to the all-knowing, all-powerful God.

Prayer is a process in which we speak to God. Meditation is a process in which we listen.

This 'God' is not just the all-knowing creator but also the God that lies within each and every one of us. This God manifests as intuition, inspiration, and enthusiasm, which all spark our energy levels and can enrich our spiritual life greatly.

Prayer and meditation are partners, and just as in any relationship, two-way communication is essential. From an Eastern perspective, prayer is yang and meditation is yin, working in harmony with each other. If one side dominates the conversation, it affects the relationship.

The same applies to our relationship with God. We benefit by talking and by listening to God. This sheds light on the popular phrase 'I am going to meditate on it' when dealing with life's issues.

Grandmom's Eulogy

It was very early one morning in 2009. I had just moved into my quiet cabin retreat outside Gettysburg, Pennsylvania. I woke up around four am, wide awake for no apparent reason, so I did some yoga postures and meditation. Both had become part of my morning routine since my return from India the previous year.

During my meditations, I often reach a point where my body and mind become very still and calm. My breathing becomes very long and slow and I let go of errant thoughts as I enter a state of deep relaxation. While in this state, even though my mind is relatively empty of thoughts, I often receive insights on life's challenges and creative inspiration for my work.

This time my meditation was very different. As I relaxed, thoughts about my grandmother entered my mind for no apparent reason. Thoughts and words about her life poured into my mind, flowed through me and filled me. It was as if I was downloading information about her life.

My grandmother was still alive, a wonderful woman who had led a tough life, although most would consider her ordinary. She didn't possess a college degree, never held a professional job, and suffered with many physical and emotional issues. Although I loved my grandmother, we were not especially close because I saw her only once or twice a year during family visits.

Nevertheless, that morning, information about her life poured through me like I was watching a documentary with beautiful, well-articulated ideas and descriptions of her life and the virtuous things she did. The story made her seem to be a spiritual superhero. I was so moved, I cried. My cats watched in obvious astonishment as I reached continuously for the tissue box.

After I was done with the 'download,' I sat and tried to regain my composure. At the time, I didn't understand what had happened, but it felt like I had just watched an inspiring tearjerker movie. I realized what a perfect tribute this would be for my grandmother. I came to believe that this tribute was divinely created and was to be her eulogy when she passed.

At this emotional moment, I opened my laptop and sent my aunt Chrissy an email, asking her if I could say Grandmom's eulogy if she passed before I did. Aunt Chrissy is my mom's younger sister and was my grandmother's caretaker at the time.

Then I went back to sleep.

When I woke up the next morning, I was able to digest what had happened in the middle of the night. I came to my senses a bit and called Aunt Chrissy, explaining to her what had occurred in the night and apologizing for the overenthusiastic eulogy request. Chrissy was actually excited to hear about my experience and was more than happy to let me have the honor of speaking on Grandmom's behalf.

When my grandmother passed some months later, Chrissy phoned to ask if I still had that eulogy ready to present at the funeral. I accepted the job happily, although the eulogy didn't exist on paper yet, only in my head.

Once I had it written down, my only concern was how to present the eulogy without blubbering. Each time I rehearsed it, I was moved to tears and went through at least one full box of tissues.

At the funeral service at the church, I gave the eulogy, and I made it through without crying. As I expected, everyone loved it. I felt inspired and honored to celebrate my grandmother in such a fitting way.

This, I think, is an ideal example of what people mean by saying 'I'm going to meditate on it.' During hectic, emotional lives, we often make hasty, irrational decisions we later regret. Sometimes we struggle for inspiration on projects or problems. When we quiet the analytical mind during meditation, the spiritual mind awakens. Our emotions, thoughts, ego, and analytical mind can impede our soul's ability to provide intuition and divine guidance. Through meditation, we are awakening the 'Kingdom of God' that lies dormant inside us. I believe this is the same 'Kingdom' that Jesus spoke of in the Bible and that he himself awakened during his many meditative journeys.

Meditation at Sunday Mass

Meditation is a universally practiced art around the world. For most religions, meditation is the cornerstone of their spiritual practices. It is also being welcomed into civil society. Police departments are initiating programs for officers to practice meditation in Canada and the U.S. to alleviate job-related stress and improve instincts and reflexes. Elementary schools have built meditation into their lessons and found that children were less anxious and hyperactive and got better grades.

Science shows such health benefits from daily meditation that it could be the ultimate cure-all 'pill,' inexpensive and with few side effects. Meditation stimulates areas of our brain that affect compassion, which could cure violence in our society and promote the most fundamental spiritual law that Buddha, Krishna and Jesus all preached: to love and only to love.

I believe the time has come for Christians around the world to benefit from meditation. I would love walk into Sunday mass knowing that a twenty-minute meditation will be part of the service. Christians of all denominations deserve the opportunity to strive for the kingdom of heaven (Luke 17:21) as Jesus inspired us to.

Spiritual Exercise: Meditation

Sit somewhere that is quiet and comfortable. You may sit straight in a chair with feet flat on the floor or in the lotus position on the floor.

Close your eyes and bring your attention to your breathing.

Breathe slowly, deeply, gently, and inaudibly, in and out through your nose.

Bring all of your attention to your breath and how the air feels entering your body. Feel the nostrils take in the air, the lungs filling, the abdomen expanding on each inhalation. Upon each exhalation, feel the air exit your body as the abdomen and chest collapse downward.

As random thoughts enter your mind, simply let them go and continue focusing entirely on your breath. Do not become frustrated when thoughts enter your mind; this is a natural part of the process. Just let them go when they arise.

Continue breathing for as long as you wish. You may practice this exercise every day for one to five minutes. When you've become skilled at focusing on the breath, with few thoughts entering your mind, then increase by five minutes until you eventually reach up to sixty minutes.

This is meditation. The benefits are endless.

Chapter Eleven:
Faith and Healing

Faith and Mind Power

Carried away by the burst of vitality that flowed from practicing qigong and the subsequent improvement in my health, I was overdoing the tennis and basketball. The strain began taking its toll on my tall, thin body and my knee problems returned.

It was 2005, my second season of playing USTA tennis, and our team was making another deep run and quest to get back to the National Tournament. I was again put to the test, playing even stronger competition in my singles matches.

Jesus replied, '...Truly I tell you,
if you have faith as small as a mustard seed,
you can say to this mountain,
'Move from here to there,' and it will move.
Nothing will be impossible for you.'

Matthew 17:20

In addition to our team being bumped up a level, to 3.5, after making Nationals the previous year, we also added another team, so we were now competing in both Maryland and Virginia.

My right knee had been bothering me toward the end of the season, but I was confident that a bit of rest when the playoffs ended would be enough to heal it. I played a grueling match against a talented player in Newport News, Virginia on Sunday morning, and immediately drove three hours to Columbia, Maryland for yet another challenging playoff match against an even tougher opponent in the afternoon. Both players chased me around the court like a wild caged monkey. I was literally scaling the fence at times, trying to return my opponents' overpowering shots. By the end of the day, which was also the end of our season, I was hurting. I got home, went to bed, and didn't move for four hours. When I got up again, I couldn't bend my right knee without loud crunching and a lot of pain.

This led to a rare trip to the doctor. The orthopedic physician did an MRI, which showed cartilage damage and microfractures in my knee. He suggested rest and a lot of ice and heating. If it didn't improve in a few months, I would need surgery to clean things up. I left his clinic confident that I could heal myself with Chinese medicine and other natural methods.

I gave my knee time and smothered it with all sorts of natural methods to promote its proper healing. However, after more than four years of pampering, my knee improved only slightly. I was able to hike and walk, but anything like tennis or basketball was painful and difficult. My normally positive outlook dimmed and I slowly allowed negative thoughts to creep into my psyche, such as 'Well, I guess my knee will never heal.' I often thought, 'There's not much else I can do. I suppose that I have to live with this for the rest of my life.'

When I first noticed these thought patterns, I became alert. I had observed the effects of negative thought patterns in relationship to my patients' poor health, and decided to take charge.

At this stage, I also considered surgery, since it was a relatively simple procedure to clean up the cartilage damage. But when I asked patients and friends who had undergone the same procedure, only a few reported good long-term success. Most said it didn't help much, and some said it made the problem worse. I decided to exhaust all other options first.

During my qigong studies, I learned mind training—called *shengong*—which is essential for an effective healer. We trained our mind, much like a muscle, to think positive healing thoughts all the time. Our minds have the power to heal, and there is no better tool than what's inside our head.

I decided to see if my mind could assist in the healing. I obtained a picture of a healthy knee joint and hung a copy of the picture in my study and another in my bedroom. I also created a simple healing affirmation: 'My knees are in perfect health.'

At every opportunity I looked at the picture, then closed my eyes and visualized the healthy knee joint as my own. Whenever doubts about my knee entered my mind, I stopped the thought and repeated my affirmation over and over. 'My knees are in perfect health. My knees are in perfect health.'

Within a year, my knee improved and gradually I played sports again.

Although I had seen the power of the mind work for others, the healing of my own knee amazed me. I believe my thoughts and visualizations created the reality that I envisioned.

Several years later, I'm still playing ball against players many years younger than me, without discomfort or pain.

The concept that thoughts have actual power is not 'New Age' nonsense. Many studies have demonstrated the power of the mind. When athletes visualize their routine, the same neurons that fire in the brain are activated as during their actual performance. In a study, weight lifters who trained hard over a three-month period achieved a thirty percent increase in muscle strength—while weight lifters who only visualized their workout routine but performed no actual lifting still saw a significant thirteen percent increase in muscle strength.

Our thoughts create our reality. So, if you don't want to be fat, then stop telling yourself that you *are* fat.

If you want to be healthy, stop thinking of poor health.

If negative thought patterns are deeply engrained in your psyche, you can change these patterns with the proper mental training. By first letting go of the emotions that fuel the negative thought patterns, we can begin the healing process and transformation of the mind.

Our minds not only have physical and mental power but are connected with our spirit as well. The spiritual power of our minds connects us with God and awakens the God-like qualities within us.

Jesus only used virtuous and loving words when he spoke, and I'm sure he also held those thoughts in his mind and heart. I imagine that when Jesus healed others, walked on water, or turned water into wine, he was using the manifesting power of his own mind. He never let fear or doubt enter his psyche, and told us to do the same. 'You can move mountains if you simply have faith.'

When I first started my private practice many years ago, I paid little attention to my patients' thoughts, emotions, or faith in relationship with how they healed. I took each case separately and did my best to get them well. However, over time I noticed how my patients' emotional state and thoughts affected how they healed under my care.

I observed that the virtue of faith played the biggest role. When patients had faith, they healed better and faster. Whether this was their faith in God, faith in their own body's healing ability, or faith in the therapist's work, it did not matter.

It is our faith that heals us if we simply believe.

In the Bible, Jesus' mention of faith was the most common ingredient to his miracles. Healing the sick time and time again, he said that it was the recipient's faith that healed them. So Jesus was essentially giving the credit to us, as well as to our God-given abilities.

Jesus was particularly impressed with the great faith of the centurion as he healed his paralyzed servant (Matthew 8: 5-13). Jesus questioned the blind men who sought healing whether they believed that they could be cured. Seeing their faith, he restored their health (Matthew 9: 27-31). When Jesus exorcised the boy with the evil spirit, he explained to his father that *he* could also heal his son, if he simply believed (Mark 9:22-24). Jesus observed his disciples' lack of faith while at sea during a strong storm. Frustrated that they didn't realize the power of their own minds, which had become filled with fear, Jesus amazed them by calming the storm and walking on water (Matthew 8:23-27).

Many of my patients who seek my care are experiencing acupuncture for the first time. There's often a good deal of anxiety and skepticism, but also some level of faith in Chinese medicine. Anyone who doesn't think that acupuncture could possibly help wouldn't give it a try at all.

Faith plays a role in other aspects of our lives as well. For one thing, it is an essential aspect of any marriage. We need faith in ourselves to accomplish anything, and faith in our co-workers and team-mates to accomplish group goals.

Highly successful people often possess great confidence in themselves and the possibilities the universe provides. As a sports fan, I always marvel at athletes who, after a big win, say in interviews that it was their belief in themselves and in their teammates that pushed them over the top. No matter how many doubted their abilities, they had faith in themselves to accomplish their goals.

When I first started my practice years ago, I was timid in my approach and lacked full confidence in myself as a healer. However, after years of practicing, I gained experience and trust in Chinese medicine and my ability to administer it. As with any craft or art, more experience gives greater confidence.

My growing confidence translated into more trust from my patients. This in turn led to greater belief in myself as a healer and thus to better results.

I worked for a very successful Chinese acupuncturist shortly after I graduated from acupuncture school. I saw how he promoted himself to local physicians and potential patients as one of the finest practitioners in town. At the time, I found this to be a bit arrogant. Now I see that his self-promotion inspired his patients to greater faith in him as a healer. Whether or not he was the best in town didn't matter. What counted was that he and his patients believed it. Patients walked in the door with the conviction that they were about to receive treatment from the best acupuncturist around. They believed they would be healed, and they usually were. I saw how their enormous faith in this man led to more effective results.

On the flip side, you could be a highly-skilled, knowledgeable healer, but if you lack faith in your abilities, how effective will you be at healing your patients? And if your patients lack faith in you, that will also affect your results.

Even Jesus himself was ineffective healing in his hometown. The people there could not believe that 'the carpenter's son' who they had known since he was a boy, could perform such feats. Jesus didn't perform many healings there because of the lack of faith (Mark 6:4). No matter how good a healer you are, if the ingredient of faith is missing, the results will indeed be impaired.

I see this so often in my patients' ability to get better, and have come to believe that sometimes the treatment itself doesn't even matter much. Whether it's a drug, an herb, an acupuncture needle, or a sugar pill, if there is great faith the outcome will often be positive.

To be clear, acupuncture works well with or without the effect of one's mind. Double-blind studies have proven this many times over. It also works well on animals, and I don't think they have preconceived notions or beliefs before their treatment. I've witnessed many a skeptic turn believer with acupuncture treatments in my own practice. The power of the mind only enhances the efficacy of any medical treatment.

Although evangelical 'faith healers' sometimes get a bad rap and are often called con men, I understand why they are so effective. The people who come to be healed believe in the process, and the faith healers themselves demonstrate the same confident faith. In addition, the crowds of sometimes thousands also have a great belief that healing will happen. Faith is a potent energy that drives the healing process. With so much faith, the outcome can often be 'miraculous.'

I was treating a patient with acupuncture one time and I added electrical stimulation to the needles, which is a common adjunct therapy in Chinese medicine. The patient waited as I hooked up the clips to the needles. She knew what to expect, since I had treated her with e-stim before. After everything was set up, I turned on the e-stim unit and gradually increased the intensity. As the volume reached 4-5, which was when she usually felt the electrical sensations and signaled me to stop, she didn't say anything. I increased the intensity further. Then it came. Her foot twitched noticeably and she chirped, 'Okay, I feel it!'

I finished the treatment as usual and she felt better. As we concluded, I saw the electrical socket. The unit was not plugged in!

We both had utmost faith that the unit was on and believed that there was electrical stimulation to points in her feet. She felt the current strongly, and I saw her foot twitch. This shows the power of the mind in creating our own reality.

Faith also plays a role in Western medicine. Scientific studies show that faith and the mind have a significant role in a patient's ability to heal. However, the Western medical community doesn't use the terms 'belief' or 'faith healing.' Allopathic medicine refers to it as the 'placebo effect.' Instead of fostering the power of the mind, doctors view the placebo effect as an annoying statistical anomaly and dismiss its relevance.

The placebo effect is not a deception or statistical anomaly, but a product of anticipation based on faith.

When I talk to friends who doubt the effects of acupuncture or holistic medicine entirely, even when I refer to successfully treated patients, they often say, 'It's all in their head,' or 'They just wanted it to work,' or 'It's just a placebo effect.'

The irony about these belief patterns is that they all suggest the power of the mind is greater than the therapy itself. If you acknowledge the 'placebo effect,' you are essentially backing Jesus' teachings of the power of faith. More so, you are supporting the most natural and holistic healing method of them all, which is the power of a person's own mind.

Although faith is often associated with religion, it really just represents the power of our own minds. Faith has an enormous energy that can manifest a potential healing effect. So often, with our health, we have to be 'spoon fed' our faith in the form of double-blind scientific studies. We've been trained to doubt any form of healing that hasn't been proven through multi-million dollar studies.

In the West, scientists analyze the mind from a purely physical perspective. We analyze the brain and the millions of cellular activities that take place within the vast network of neurons and cells and the many neurotransmitters that perform functions within the body.

From an Eastern perspective, the mind is observed on a much deeper level. The Daoists word 'shen' represents the mind but has a much broader meaning. Shen not only includes the physical and mental faculties but the consciousness associated with our minds. Shen is associated with yet another energy center in the head called the upper dantian. In Daoist alchemy and qigong tradition, shengong training involves any training of the mind, which includes mental (brain) and spiritual (consciousness) aspects.

The Daoist alchemists viewed the three dantians as cauldrons, and utilized them for gathering and converting vital energies and aspects of consciousness. Each of the three dantians has been mentioned separately throughout this book. The lower dantian is like the battery where we store energy. The middle dantian is associated with the heart and the virtues of love and compassion, where our emotional energies can be processed and transformed. This purified energy can then be guided up the spine to where it stimulates the upper dantian, where psychic perceptions and intuitive awareness come about. This can lead the apprentice towards higher communications, experiences of intense bliss, and perceptions that transcend time and space.

Therefore, the power of faith relates not only to the power of our physical mind but our spiritual mind as well. I think the old saying, 'We only use ten percent of our minds,' is true, but that other ninety percent is right there for the taking. By utilizing ancient methods to effectively train the mind, we can 'move mountains' as Jesus told us.

Everything in this world must first be created in thought. The clearer our thoughts are, the more effective creators we become. Adding a strong dose of faith magnifies our thought potential.

As the Bible says, 'As a person thinks in his heart, so he will become' (Proverbs 23:7). We often allow the static of excessive worry and negative thoughts to dilute our thought potential. Our thoughts create our reality, and the element of faith helps us maximize the power of our minds. Jesus told us that the mind can heal, and science has proven this point. Through mind training, affirmation, prayer, and meditation, we can unleash that untapped ninety percent of our minds that may allow us to heal from all diseases.

Chapter Twelve:
Seeing the Light

When I was fifteen years old, I was at St. Catherine's Church in my hometown during Holy Week. I remember the annual celebration of Christ's death and resurrection as a solemn and reverent time for Christians. There were several special masses to celebrate Jesus' death and resurrection. As altar boys, we had extra duties to perform at this time.

On Good Friday, we observed the Stations of the Cross at seven pm. Afterwards, two altar boys knelt in front of the Holy Eucharist (Holy Communion), which was held in a special tabernacle during Holy Week. We acted as guards to the Holy Eucharist and rotated every half-hour from eight pm until midnight. The Church would be left

Let your light shine before men in such a way that they may see your good works, and glorify your Father who is in heaven.

Matthew 5:16

open for twenty-four hours so that members of the congregation could come and pray and pay reverence. This was a solemn, respectful time free of any talking, just silence and prayer in contemplation of how Jesus had died on the cross for all mankind.

I vividly recall the weight of the silence. Maybe it was the profound stillness or pondering the magnitude of Jesus' life and death, but at that moment, I could feel his presence in the Church. I wondered what it would be like to fully know and experience Jesus firsthand. I knew that, technically speaking, Jesus was always with us, but what might it be like to experience his light and love in a more tangible fashion? When I died and went to heaven, I would experience Jesus, but could I experience him fully on this earthly realm?

Many years ago, early in my acupuncture practice, a man came for treatment and opened up about a religious experience he had decades before during a Christian retreat.

The retreat lasted several weeks and involved long periods of meditation and prayer. In the midst of one such period, what occurred was far beyond anything he had ever experienced. He went into a state of bliss and ecstasy that surpassed any earthly description. He no longer felt his body. Instead, he had a sensation of light and love so powerful that he was overwhelmed. The light intensified, and he knew in his heart that the light was that of Jesus Christ.

I was fascinated. My first question was, 'How did you know it was Jesus Christ?'

He said he didn't see a face, just an intense light that he described as being hundreds of times brighter than any light of the earthly realm, but amazingly did not blind him. The intense innate presence of Jesus Christ was accompanied by an engulfing feeling of love, which also was 'hundreds' of times greater than any love he had experienced during his lifetime.

Again I asked him how he could be sure it was Jesus Christ. He assured me that, although he could not see a body or face, he knew with absolute certainty that it was Jesus and felt his immeasurable compassion and love. I told him that I believed him, but my scientific mind was still trying to fully grasp what he had encountered. I asked if he may have been dreaming or hallucinating. Maybe it was some trickery that his mind was playing on him. He assured me with conviction that his experience was the most profound and genuine he had ever been through. What he felt was a hundred times more pleasurable than anything he had ever experienced on earth or in any dream state. His faith in the afterlife and in Jesus Christ became stronger than ever after this encounter and he no longer fears death.

Within a year, I met two more people who described similar experiences to me. One was an Eastern Indian man I met at one of Amma's blessings on the East coast. We spoke about several spiritual matters and he described an experience he called 'seeing the light.'

The one major difference was that he didn't mention Jesus Christ specifically, although he said it was the light of God. Could the deity you worshipped influence the kind of divine experience you might have? He described an enormous feeling of light and love and said it was many times more pleasurable than any experience on the earthly realm.

A few months later, while working at George Washington University's Center for Integrative Medicine in Washington, DC, I met a Catholic nun who was studying holistic medicine and interning at our clinic. She observed one of my medical qigong treatment sessions and we chatted afterwards. She asked many questions about the ancient healing art, and then I asked some questions too.

I recounted what these people had told me about their amazing experiences. She said, 'Oh yes, it sounds like they had an illumination.' She explained that this was a common experience for many Christian nuns and monks after prolonged periods of fasting, prayer, and meditation, herself included.

Years later, after meeting Brother Seif, I came to understand that many Christian saints have described similar experiences after prolonged periods of asceticism. These Godly encounters are common in many religions and have different names: illuminations, divine ecstasies, union with God, seeing the light, or religious experiences.

St. Teresa of Avila and John of the Cross, both Roman Catholic saints and named Doctors of the Church by Pope Paul VI, shared their personal journeys and laid out detailed plans on how to attain these mystical states through contemplation and prayer. Their books, *Interior Castle, Dark Night of the Soul,* and *The Way of Perfection,* detail specific methods for developing personal growth of the soul. They define this ultimate spiritual state as 'obtaining union with God.'

St. Teresa advocates that God wishes union with each of us, even in this lifetime. She also states, like many Eastern yogis and qigong masters, that spiritual favors and supernatural gifts should never to be expected or pursued. They occur naturally during the humble pursuit of union and are granted by God alone.

She advises consistent prayer and meditation along with a willingness to give up the 'things of this world.' Like my friends who have had these experiences, she says that there is no way to describe the 'riches and treasure and delights' during the mystical union, and that they are beyond any earthly pleasure.

Some religions call this state nirvana, some call it enlightenment, some call it union with God, and some call it heaven on earth.

Hinduism refers to this state as *samadhi,* an intense state of concentration achieved through meditation in which the meditator reaches spiritual ecstasy through union with God. Paramahansa Yogananda, in *Autobiography of a Yogi,* describes this state in detail:

'Samadhi is a joyous experience, a splendid light in which you behold the countless worlds floating in a vast bed of joy and bliss. Banish the spiritual ignorance that makes you think this mortal life is real. Have these beautiful experiences for yourself in eternal Samadhi, in God. Auroras of light, skyfuls of eternal bliss will be opened to you. Forget your dream-born mortal weakness. Wake up and know that you and God are one.'

I was so amazed that people could have these heavenly encounters. If these real-life, blissful experiences with God were indeed true and could be attained by ordinary people, perhaps I didn't have to wait until the end of my life either to feel God. I figured that if there was an earthly state several times more enjoyable than anything I had ever known, I wanted to figure out a way to attain it.

I learned that a devoted aspirant could attain glimpses of this blissful state, but that evolved masters can achieve it at will.

Athletes describe a related experience of heightened senses during athletic events. This state, often termed 'the zone,' involves complete focus. Everything slows down, time no longer exists, and action becomes effortless. Individuals may feel invincible, and are often able to anticipate their opponents' next move and to 'make every shot.'

I'll never forget watching point guard Isiah Thomas in the 1988 NBA Finals versus the Lakers. For years, Isiah had fought to unseat Larry Bird and Magic Johnson as NBA champion. But in Game 6, with his team closing in on the title, Isiah severely sprained his ankle and hobbled to the bench. Unable to put weight on his leg, with his foot swollen like a balloon, he covered his eyes in frustration, knowing that his team could not win without him. Then, after a few moments of stillness, his eyes opened with a laser beam focus and he told his stunned coach that he wanted to go back into the game.

Limping around for almost an entire half, barely able to put any pressure on his foot, he went into a transformation. He hit shot after shot, finishing the third quarter with an NBA Finals record 25 points. Thomas describes this state:

'It's almost like you're two steps ahead of every player, it's almost like slow motion. You get to see everything. I got an energy burst somewhere. It just happened. It's like your total game comes together in those four or five minutes...You can't really feel it. It just happens. Boom, it's there. You just kind of smile. Right then, at that moment, you're not even thinking. Just feeling. Feeling real good.'

In his renowned book *Flow: The Psychology of Optimal Experience*, psychologist Mihaly Csikszentmihalyi defines 'flow' as a state of concentration so focused that ego falls away. According to Csikszentmihalyi, this deeply satisfying state—which is particularly associated with the creative process—is at the root of what makes us happy. In common with the athletes' description of 'the zone,' the experiencer loses track of time yet feels alert, in control, and connected to something greater than oneself. The ability to experience this phenomenon is universal and isn't confined to particular cultures or activities.

Many Catholic saints and holy people encourage ordinary people to seek this experience. Father Thomas Dubay (1921-2010) was an American Catholic priest who spent much of his adult life preaching the importance of prayer and deep meditation. He was a strong advocate of every person's birthright to experience union with God in this lifetime. He wrote the book *Fire Within,* which details the life and teachings of John of the Cross and St. Theresa Avila.

St. Catherine of Siena (1347-1380) is believed to have entered into divine ecstasy with the Lord many times. Once, while in spiritual ecstasy for five straight days, she spoke the contents of a book, *The Dialogue,* which her peers transcribed.

Julian of Norwich (1342-1416) was a Christian mystic from England who fell gravely ill when she was thirty. Seemingly on her deathbed, she had numerous visions of Jesus Christ and received revelations that she referred to as 'showings.' In *Revelations of Love,* the first book in the English language by a woman, Julian wrote about these showings and about our connection to God the Almighty Father:

'Greatly ought we to rejoice that God dwells in our soul; and more greatly ought we rejoice that our soul dwells in God. It is nothing else than right understanding, with true belief and certain trust in our being, that we are in God, and he is in us, which we do not see.'

Jesus not only confirms this potential union with God, but also that 'we do not see,' when he speaks in parables:

'The Kingdom of Heaven may be compared to a king who gave a wedding feast for his son, and sent his servants to call those who were invited to the wedding feast, but they would not come. Again he sent his servants, saying 'Tell those who are invited, see, I have prepared my dinner, my oxen and my fat calves have been slaughtered, and everything is ready. Come to the wedding feast.' But they paid no attention and went off, one to his farm, another to his business. For many are invited, but few are chosen' (Matthew 22: 1-14).

In a post on an online Catholic forum, this woman describes her overpowering encounter of spiritual euphoria and wonders why more people do not talk about it:

'I go into ecstasy whenever I connect to God through prayer or meditation. The sensation is so powerful and so overwhelming, that it completely takes away even severe pain and leaves me feeling euphoric. I honestly think I could have surgery without anesthetic and not feel a thing if I was in such a state. I don't even have the words to describe it. It's like Divine love is pouring into you, until you feel as if you're glowing with ethereal light. It's very powerful and life changing, and I just wonder why people don't talk about it. I know I'm not the only one!'

The 'zone' or 'flow' in athletes, as defined by Csikszentmihalyi, is an intense focus on the activity the individual is engrossed in. Paramahansa Yogananda also mentions this intense concentration, within meditation, as a necessary ingredient in attempts to capture this heightened spiritual state:

'Meditation utilizes concentration in its highest form. Concentration consists in freeing the attention from distractions and in focusing it on any thought in which one may be interested. Meditation is that special form of concentration in which the attention has been liberated from restlessness and is focused on God. Meditation, therefore, is concentration to know God.'

After reading of these light phenomena, I now view Jesus' frequent mention of light from a new perspective. Jesus told us that the light would shine on us (John 12:35-37). He told us that the Kingdom of Heaven is within and that we could attain union with him. 'That they all may be one; as you, Father, are in me, and I in you, they also may be one with us so that the world may believe that you have sent me' (John 17:21). 'I am the light of the world. Whoever follows me will never walk in darkness, but will have the light of life' (John 8:12).

Although I practice the suggested paths of meditation, fasting, and prayer, I have yet to yield this blissful state for myself. But I'm not giving up. I plan to continue my humble path on the quest in hope that someday God grants me a glimpse of this transcendent experience.

Chapter Thirteen:
Our Spiritual Anatomy

I'll never forget packing into Goessmann Lab auditorium during my freshman year at the University of Massachusetts in 1989 for anatomy and physiology class. The instructor went over organs, muscles, glands, tendons, and bones, whipping through slide after slide on the projector in the front of the large classroom, while I and over 150 other students frantically tried to keep up and take notes.

During those lectures, I grasped what a fascinating creation the human body is, with millions of cells operating in perfect harmony with one another. Anyone doubting an all-powerful creator only has to look at this wondrous design to appreciate the higher power that created this realm.

Don't you know that your body is God's temple and that God's Spirit dwells in you?

1 Corinthians 3:16

Every person of faith knows that our bodies are much more than physical tissue and that we possess an eternal soul. The Bible says that our bodies are a temple of God and that the Spirit of God is within us all, but it doesn't give specifics about our spiritual anatomy. In the gospels, Jesus describes an energy that lies within our bodies. The words 'power,' 'light,' and 'virtue' are used to name the energy that is most often linked with his miracle healings.

What is not explained in The Bible is exactly *how* Jesus performed these amazing healings. Nor does it provide a detailed description of our energetic and spiritual bodies. Throughout this book, energy has been spoken about extensively. The energetic anatomy has been detailed from an Eastern perspective. Let's take a closer look at the subtle energetic anatomy that lies within us and how it is associated with our health, healing abilities, and quest for spiritual awakening.

Rivers of Energy

The first time I saw a picture of the acupuncture meridians was in 1995, when I began studies in Chinese medicine. My acupressure teacher, Sam McClellan, showed us charts with various lines on the body and points along these pathways. I felt a sense of wonder at them. It made sense to me that God would wire us with an electrical system that allowed us to heal ourselves.

Since that day, I've dedicated much of my life to the study of these meridians and how they work within the body, both from textbooks and from over twenty years' experience in my clinic.

The phenomena that occur when a patient comes to my office for treatment still astonish me. Most patients want to know exactly how acupuncture works. I explain the basic concept and ask them to lie down on the table so they get to experience it for themselves. They rest with a pillow under their head and another under their knees. I insert several hair-thin needles into their body at various locations, and we wait for the magic to take place as the qi in their body begins to percolate.

Some patients tell me that they feel warmth and tingling up their arms and legs and into their torso, like a soft electrical current. I often ask them to point to the path of the sensation. Often, they identify precisely the meridian I stimulated—without previous knowledge where those meridians are or even which points I have needled.

Others will experience spontaneous limb movements and feelings of lightness, as if about to float off of the table. Most patients enjoy the subtle energetic sensation and associated tranquility.

One patient told me that she felt her arms lifting up off the table while I was out of the room during the session, and was amazed when I came back and told her they were still lying flat just as they had been when I left. But during the following week's session, when I came to take her needles out, her arms *were* floating up off the table! I knew she wasn't doing it on purpose because she was fast asleep.

Another common manifestation is when I hear patients' bile ducts open just seconds after I inserted an acupuncture needle at Liver-3 and Gallbladder-34. These classic points help to stimulate energy flow into the liver and gallbladder and often initiate the release of congested bile. I just smile when patients hear the gurgling and squirting sounds in their abdomen and typically say, 'Oh, excuse me, I must be getting hungry.'

Until about twenty years ago, many people here in the United States thought of acupuncture therapy as 'voodoo' and quackery, despite thousands of years of success in the East.

After double-blinded studies at the U. S. National Institute of Health and throughout the world, and the development of instruments that can detect energy within the body, the mainstream Western medical community has finally given the stamp of approval to acupuncture.

Auras

Most pictures of Jesus Christ show a glowing aura around his head, and some also depict light radiating from his body while he heals the sick. As a child I assumed this was simply to convey Jesus' holiness.

But auras are a true manifestation of energy around people and objects. Most people can see hazy heat waves above the ground on a hot summer day. Those are more obvious and easier to see than auras. Our bodies also emit energy and heat, but usually so subtly that most people can't see it. Saints and holy persons resonate at a higher frequency and thus radiate more energy from their bodies, which can be more easily detected by the naked eye. Paintings of Jesus present a bright aura around his body because that's what people saw.

In my first years as an acupuncturist, I wasn't sure whether auras existed, but now I'm a firm believer, and I train students to view auras as a means of diagnosing their patients.

The incident that convinced me happened when I treated an interesting patient named Naomi. During the initial consultation, I explained acupuncture and energy to her. She told me that she already understood the concept of energy and casually mentioned that she could see auras. Unconvinced, but fascinated, I stepped outside my professional box for a moment and asked about her unusual skill. Would she read my aura?

Twice before, on separate occasions, patients had told me that my aura was blue. Would Naomi say the same? She looked at the area just above my head and said that she saw a beautiful blue aura. I hadn't taken the first two impressions seriously, but this third observation intrigued me, and I wanted to find out more.

195

The next week I had a cancellation just before Naomi's appointment. I spent a half hour performing a meditation in which I visualized radiant blue light entering my kidneys and overflowing the rest of my body. When Naomi arrived, I greeted and treated her as usual. While she rested with the needles in her, I asked her if she would read my aura again. I didn't mention my 'blue' meditation.

She told me that she saw the same blue aura—but much brighter and more radiant then last week. Again, I was impressed.

I asked her what her husband thought of her gift. She had never told him during their twenty-three years of marriage because she was afraid of what he might think. She told me that when she was a kid, having the gift of seeing auras was not a 'cool' thing. Whenever she told people what colors and lights were above their head, everyone thought she was crazy, and she got mocked at school. So Naomi quietly went about her life, telling only a few individuals about her ability.

Perhaps people feel more comfortable talking about otherworldly experiences to an acupuncturist than to others. Experiences like these with my patients deepen my faith in this work beyond anything I've learned from textbooks or my teachers.

Years ago, at the end of a qigong class, one of my students told me about attending a talk by a Hindu saint who was visiting the United States. Among hundreds of people, he waited in the auditorium for the saint to arrive. Moments before the saint entered, my student saw a white light permeating one of the back walls near a set of double doors. The light gradually became more pronounced, and then the saint and several other people entered through the door. He realized with wonder that the light he had witnessed was the aura surrounding the saint's body.

Kirlian photography and infrared photography devices can detect and measure energy fields that surround living things, from plants to human beings. The naked eye cannot normally see these auras. However, evolved beings such as Jesus, Buddha, and Krishna radiated so much energy that even untrained people could often see it.

When someone is in excellent physical health, the aura around their body is often thick and bright, and when they are in poor health, the energy fields can be greatly diminished. In Chinese medicine we call these energy fields 'wei qi,' and by scanning a person's wei qi we can pick up on subtle imbalances in the body.

Often, while treating patients with medical qigong, I can detect these energy fields with my palms as I scan their body. I look for soft spots, holes, and stagnation, which indicate where and to what degree the disease has manifested.

It's exciting for me as a teacher to see my students witness auras in class for the first time. Students often tell me that they can see my aura while I'm teaching. When a person speaks or acts with enthusiasm and passion, their aura tends to become more pronounced.

Energy fields surrounding the body protect us from physical and energetic invasion of pathogens, warn us of dangers, and pick up on the emotional states of the people with whom we interact regularly. Often, when I see patients with extreme allergies, chemical sensitivities, cancer, depression, or chronic fatigue syndrome, their wei qi fields are typically very diminished and even collapsed around their body.

Chakras

While working for the George Washington University in 2003, just a year before I started my training in medical qigong in California, I received my first reiki energy healing session. Sara was a massage therapist who had just started working for the center. We did an exchange—I gave her an acupuncture treatment and she gave me a massage. She asked if I wanted to try some reiki healing as well. Since I knew little about reiki at the time, I asked a few questions and was happy to accept the opportunity.

As I lay on my back, she asked if I ever had my chakras balanced. I had heard about chakras, but didn't know much about them. Sara explained that all humans had energy centers located along the center core of the body, close to the spine at the level of each endocrine gland. She told me how the word chakra meant 'wheel' in

Sanskrit. Each chakra was like a spiraling wheel of energy that spun outwards from the body in a small cone or vortex. To help me understand further, she used the analogy of a chakra as a fan that distributed heat throughout a house. Your chakras help to distribute and balance energy within the body to maintain optimal health. When a chakra is blocked, congested, overactive, or deficient, this could manifest as energy not being able to nourish a certain organ or gland and thus create a range of possible symptoms.

She then informed me that she would dangle a pendulum above each energy center. If the chakra were balanced and healthy, the pendulum would move clockwise. If a chakra were out of balance, the pendulum would rotate counter-clockwise. The more pronounced the rotation, the more indicative of a possibly overactive or deficient condition within the body.

Skeptical but curious, I watched her slowly and carefully hang the pendulum over various spots along my body's midline. The pendulum did indeed rotate, while the hand that held it remained perfectly still. Sara explained the significance of each movement as we went along and pointed out that the chakras on the top half of my body seemed well balanced. However, the first two, the root and naval chakras, were very blocked and she spent some time working to rebalance them.

As she worked, I asked her more about these chakras and how they might become out of balance. She informed me that the root and naval chakras often become imbalanced due to poor digestive health. I was impressed, because I did not tell her about the plethora of digestive issues I had been dealing with at that time.

When I probed further about how chakras could become imbalanced, she pointed out that our emotions can have detrimental effects on these subtle centers. She explained that the specific emotions of guilt, shame, and fear have adverse effects on the root and naval chakras. I had a flashback to the fear, guilt, and shame I suffered as a kid. Again, I was captivated by this knowledge and began taking the chakras more seriously.

When I started my training in medical qigong a year later, I became more familiar with the energetic and spiritual anatomy of the body, including chakras. Now I enjoy my students' exhilaration when they practice chakra readings with the pendulum for the first time.

As I've come to fully understand the chakra system within the body, I have also learned how these energy centers may hold the key to all health and healing. My teachers showed me how there is a fundamental energy that lies dormant within each human being, which when properly cultivated and guided can awaken the spirit within all of us.

This energy has many different names, depending on which religious tradition you examine, but is most universally known as kundalini. Kundalini is a Hindu term that means 'curl of the snake' and is often likened to a serpent force that lies coiled at the base of the spine at the first chakra. It is described as a potent form of psycho-spiritual energy. When awakened through disciplines such as yoga, meditation, and qigong, this energy rises upwards through the central channel, penetrating each chakra and eventually entering the brain.

Great vitality, power, and awareness are common effects of kundalini's ascension into the brain, the seventh chakra. This mystical experience can be fleeting for the spiritual aspirant, who may practice sporadic yet intense periods of meditation. Yogis and other evolved beings who practice meditation extensively for years have the ability to maintain the kundalini flow to the seventh chakra, providing them with a constant experience of extraordinary power, psychic ability, and sensations of ecstasy.

As my journey continued, I discovered the importance of the various energy centers along the spinal canal, not just for health and happiness. These centers could possibly hold the key to unlocking our deepest spiritual potential. When I look back at friends who've had these intense spiritual experiences, 'seeing the light,' I realize what might have been occurring. It wasn't that they were hallucinating or that they were crazy, as many may believe. They were simply experiencing an intense wakening of their souls' potential that manifested in the physical realm.

Roman Catholic minister Philip St. Romain details the phenomena of this awakening process in his book, *Kundalini Energy and Christian Spirituality: A Pathway to Growth and Healing*. As St. Romain's devout practice of mental prayer proved unrewarding, he engaged in deeper practices of contemplative prayer that quieted his mind. During these long periods of Christian meditation, he began having several physical and spiritual occurrences that were unfamiliar, to say the least. Naturally, St. Romain searched within his own Catholic tradition for answers. However, he was unable to find an explanation within the context of Christian teachings. Several conversations with nuns, priests, and his spiritual directors proved unproductive.

Confused and still searching for answers, St. Romain conducted a quest for understanding that was eventually fulfilled. He ended up discovering, in the Hindu literatures on kundalini, a detailed explanation of the sensations that were occurring within his body. Only then he was able to come to an intellectual understanding of the processes that could facilitate the deep, mystical experience that he underwent.

Although chakras are most often linked with the teachings of Buddhist, Tibetan, Hindu, and Daoist traditions, they are also recognized in other religious systems. In the Book of Revelations, Jesus speaks of various energy centers as the seven 'seals,' 'lamps,' or 'churches' (Revelations 5-8). The famous clairvoyant psychic Edgar Cayce, who predicted the 1929 stock market crash, World War II, and the earth's pole shifts, interpreted Jesus' words during one of his readings. Cayce confirmed that Jesus was indeed referring to the seven spiritual centers in the body when talking about these seven 'seals' in the book of Revelations. According to Cayce, the seven 'lamps' represent the light and wisdom that one attains from full manifestation of each chakra. The 'churches' are the seven actual churches in early Christianity in the Roman province of Asia: Epheseus, Smyrna, Pergamos, Thyatira, Sardis, Philadelphia, and Laodicea.

Paramahansa Yogananda also corroborates the link between Jesus' words in Revelations and the seven chakras in his book *The Yoga of Jesus*.

Chakras can be energized and balanced in many different ways. Our thoughts, our emotions, our diet, and our relationships all have an effect these energy centers. Physical exercise, exposure to sunlight, and limiting toxins in our environment also play a role. However, the most potent tools to awaken these centers are ascetic practices such as meditation, prayer, chanting mantras, yoga, and qigong. Therapies like medical qigong and reiki are like spiritual surgery and a wonderful way to treat unbalanced chakras.

By nourishing the chakras, the aspirant can strive to attain the light and wisdom that Jesus spoke of in the Book of Revelation. When each chakra is at full manifestation, we can experience some of the psychic gifts associated with these energy centers. Learning about the chakras and how they function helped me further understand Jesus' supernatural abilities such as clairvoyance, telepathy, prophesying, and healing.

The first chakra (root, reproductive), where the kundalini is coiled, is associated mostly with survival instincts. The second chakra (sacral, adrenal) is related to the ability of clairsentience, the capacity to pick up other people's feelings. Individuals who possess this gift are often called empaths. This is perhaps the most common psychic gift, but people often see it as a nuisance. The avalanche of emotions can overwhelm an untrained empath, exhausting them and giving them physical and emotional pain, fatigue, and other maladies. I teach my students protective meditations, which allow them to perceive others' emotions without getting overwhelmed and exhausted.

Jesus demonstrated clairsentient ability many times. For example, he perceived the Pharisees' thoughts in Matthew 12:25, he knew what the scribes were thinking while he healed the paralytic in Matthew 9:4, and he sensed the Pharisees' evil intent in plotting to trap him in his words with a question about paying taxes to Caesar in Matthew 22:18.

The third chakra (solar plexus, pancreas) is associated with psychic intuition and prophetic dreams. One of my patients told me of her travels in Europe with her husband. While driving several miles to a particular tourist spot, she got a strong intuitive sense that they should turn back. Her husband, at first frustrated, agreed, and they changed direction. Later they learned of a huge accident on that highway around the time she had her hunch.

Many patients and students have told me about their prophetic dreams. When the dreams become reality it can be a bit startling. These signs tell me that these people have naturally opened third chakras.

Jesus demonstrated the ability to foretell on many occasions, most notably when he prophesized his own death (John 12:23) and resurrection (Matthew 16:21, Mark 8:31). The Bible records other prophetic visions. During Jesus' trial, Pilate's wife had a prophetic nightmare which convinced her that Jesus was innocent and urged Pilate to free him (Matthew 27:19).

The fourth chakra (heart, thymus) relates to our ability to love unconditionally. Jesus not only preached love as his main commandment but lived it. He demonstrated it at the highest level throughout his life.

The fifth chakra (throat, thyroid) corresponds to communication and the ability of clairaudience—channeling and hearing divine voices.

At my sister's wedding dinner in 1999 in Tiburon, California, my father asked the officiating priest how he got into the priesthood. The man had never even considered the priesthood in his early adulthood. One Sunday while attending church, he heard a voice next to his right ear that said, 'You should be up there saying mass.' The clear-as-day volume of this voice baffled him, since no one was in the pew behind him.

The Bible cites many occasions when the voices of God and the angels were heard. Jesus heard them speaking to him many times. Mary and Joseph experienced several audible visits from angels announcing Jesus' birth (John 12:29, Luke 2: 8-20).

The sixth chakra (the 'third eye' or pituitary) correlates to one's aptitude to perceive someone else's thoughts, as in clairvoyance and telepathy. Do you remember the Bible story of the Samaritan woman at the well? While she initially was indifferent to Jesus, he perceived her past and told details about her relationship history. She was so impressed that, although she didn't know who he was, she proclaimed Jesus a prophet. Jesus demonstrated his clairvoyant abilities numerous times (Luke 9:47, Mark 2:8, Luke 6:8, John 2:24, John 4:17-18, Matthew 3:17).

When the crown chakra (the seventh, pineal gland) at the top of the head is stimulated, our psychic abilities are greatly enhanced. People who possess clairvoyant abilities have at least partial opening of the seventh chakra. This crown chakra also is associated with our capacity to receive messages from spirits. Jesus demonstrated his connection to God many times in the Bible, confirming his ability to communicate with the Holy Spirit and receive divine guidance. When each chakra is fully stimulated, culminating in the ascension of our consciousness to the crown of the head, we reach an enlightened state, what Jesus referred to as the 'heaven on earth' that he so often inspired us towards.

Jesus told us that we are all sons and daughters of God because we all possess the same energetic and spiritual anatomy. He inspired us to move mountains and told us that anything is possible because he was aware of our souls' potential. Jesus knew that we each had a spark of the divine within us when he said, 'Ye are Gods' (John 10:34). Being raised Catholic, I was led to believe that Jesus was on an enormous, unattainable pedestal and God lay just slightly above him on this platform. As a sinner, I was in an inescapable pit, hoping that God would take me into heaven someday after I passed from the earthly realm.

Today I feel much different about my spiritual journey on earth. I believe Jesus when he tells us that anything is possible. I believe Jesus when he told us that God is within all of us. I believe Jesus when he told us that he was the Son of God but *we too* are sons and daughters of God. I believe Jesus when he told us that others will do the same miraculous healing works as he did. I now understand why Jesus encouraged us towards virtue and love rather than fear, guilt, and anger. I now understand what Jesus means when he so often refers to allowing our light to shine forth.

It is not required to be a saint to activate these gifts. We can awaken our psychic abilities with meditations and by bringing light and energy into the chakras during our spiritual practices. As our chakras open, our abilities increase.

Some people have natural psychic abilities from birth without any particular training. Many others have innate, unrecognized gifts that develop quickly with training. Still others may be ordained or blessed directly by God with various gifts during their lifetime.

Many of these gifts are referred to as the 'clairs.' There's clairsentience (clear feeling), clairaudience (clear hearing), clairvoyance (clear seeing), and claircognizance (clear knowing). Like our physical capabilities, these metaphysical skills can be awakened with training as our energetic anatomy is ignited. All humans possess the same spiritual potential, and our physical health correlates to the balance and health of these spiritual centers within our body.

A healer can use the patient's chakras as channels for diagnosis and healing. For example, if the root chakra at the base of the spine is out of balance or blocked, the patient may exhibit physical issues that relate to the reproductive area or the colon. They may exhibit repressed anger and rage from previous abuse or addictive behaviors. Energy healing such as reiki and medical qigong is like spiritual surgery on the body and can be used to remove this blockage.

I wonder if Jesus was often balancing and energizing these chakras when he healed people of emotional problems, addictions, and psychological issues.

So when someone is ill, it may not be necessary or advisable to prescribe toxic medications and surgery. The solution can be as simple as rebalancing a chakra to restore its function, unblocking a meridian with an acupuncture needle, or rebuilding a person's wei qi field around their body.

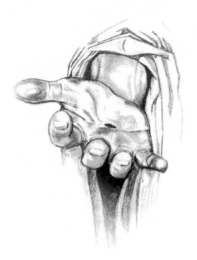

Chapter Fourteen:
Healing Like Jesus

Seeking the Guru

In 2006, I had the wonderful opportunity to go to Chengdu, China with my qigong teacher to study with one of the most revered Daoist priests in China, Abbott Zhang Ming Xin. I'll never forget the trip up to the temple. Dreamlike mountain peaks stood scattered throughout the region, with the distinctive clouds and mist hovering above and below.

Each day, we trained for a few hours at the temple near the base of the mountain with Abbott Zhang. After lunch, we had time to explore the mountain and soak up the rich history that surrounded it.

Then your light will break forth like the dawn, and your healing will quickly appear.

Isaiah 58:8

I recall the lush ancient vegetation and luxuriant organic gardens where farm workers harvested crops. The legends of holy men who spent time on the mountain fascinated me. Celestial Master Zhang used Daoist internal cultivation techniques to perfect himself and become a Daoist immortal (celestial being, enlightened one) at the age of one hundred and twenty-three.

In Chinese philosophy, the Dao is the underlying principle of the universe or the natural way in which all living things function optimally. According to the natural way, it is not uncommon for men to live well over one hundred years in excellent health. Perhaps the most famous of the Daoist immortals that meditated on this mountain is Laozi, author of the *Daodejing* (*Tao Te Ching*).

I eagerly hiked up the steep mountain one day during the break to visit some of the temples and famous caves scattered on the slope. From sheer excitement or simple forgetfulness, I failed to bring an extra sweatshirt and a hat.

Temperatures drop at the higher altitudes on Mt. Qingcheng, and the damp cold penetrates to the bones. By the time I reached the mountaintop, I was chilled.

I wanted to sit in one of the caves for a short meditation but worried about freezing my skinny butt off. Maybe it was better to hurry back down to the temple and warm up a bit.

Then I remembered a heat-inducing qigong breathing exercise I had just learned from my teacher.

I sat in the cave comfortably, with my spine straight and legs crossed, and breathed deeply into my lower dantian. I felt each breath coming into my lungs and my belly rising with each inhalation. The deep breathing brought not just ample oxygen into my body but also plentiful quantities of qi energy. Qi has a warming effect on the body, so I was confident that I could increase circulation of blood and energy to my extremities and dispel some of the cold.

I amplified the effect by visualizing the lower dantian as a small furnace. Each time I breathed in and felt my belly expand, I imagined the furnace growing hotter and hotter, much like a bellows increases fire.

Five minutes into this exercise, I was still cold. But after ten minutes, I felt some tingling and warmth in my torso, hands, and feet. A few minutes later, warmth circulated throughout my body, and before long I actually felt hot. I wasn't doing jumping jacks or any sort of vigorous exercise, and I didn't have an electric heat source under my clothing either. I was sitting quietly in a cold, damp cave, not moving. With just my breath and mind, I generated enough heat in my body that I eventually had to take my gloves off.

Small miracles like this have happened many times throughout my healing journey, but I'm still amazed when I experience the full potential of energy and spirit. Learning the mysteries of this hidden power has been a true blessing in my life.

Qigong masters, yogis, and saints have all demonstrated supernatural powers and abilities over the centuries. The ability to manifest high volumes of heat from within their body is one of the most common.

Ram Bahadur Bomjon, who was nicknamed the 'Buddha Boy,' began a several-year-long meditative stint in the forest in India when he was only sixteen years old in 2005. As his fame grew, crowds of people came to watch and film him while he meditated day and night for months on end. Without moving and without taking food (he fasted completely for extended periods), he created profound heat on several occasions. Often he appeared flushed and sweated, and more than once he burst into flames!

Many skeptics suggested that the boy was a hoax. They reasoned that he couldn't possibly have fasted for months without dying or becoming severely ill, so he must have secretly obtained food and water. But he was observed around the clock.

In all that time, he showed no signs of poor health or weight loss. His displays of heat prove that the body has the means to generate energy without food and water.

Although these phenomena strike many Westerners as odd, to Hindus and Daoists they are a typical, well-understood occurrence.

Harvard researcher Dr. Herbert Benson and his team studied Tibetan monks for years and concluded that the monks could raise their body temperature by seventeen degrees through yogic techniques. On video, the monks were shown being exposed to forty degree Fahrenheit temperatures wearing nothing but wet sheets. Within an hour, the sheets were dry. While most humans would be shivering and possibly even get sick from this exposure, the monks arose from their meditation warm, comfortable, and invigorated, much to the bewilderment of the research team.

The Body's Battery Bank

I first learned of this internal battery bank when I started my diligent practice of qigong. As detailed in chapter three, this practice led to numerous health benefits. Surprisingly, my newfound energy also transitioned into better healing results for my patients.

Before I began my daily qigong self-cultivation exercises, I treated a maximum of twenty patients per week and felt drained at the end of each day. The office where I worked at the time had three treatment rooms, and I would usually lie down in one of them for a rest between patients.

Although I dreamed of a busier practice, I didn't have the energy for it.

When I started doing qigong exercises, I gradually attained more patients. Within just the first month of qigong, I had surpassed twenty patients each week and within two months I had over thirty. When I went over forty patients per week in the fourth month, I was thrilled. The empty treatment rooms that had once provided respite for me were now filled with patients.

Extensive marketing, promotions, public presentations, and participation in health fairs the year before had only boosted my business minimally. Where did this sudden surge come from?

Surprisingly, the increased workload didn't make me tired. I felt great, had plenty of energy, and my patients were getting better results with my treatments than ever before. Could it be the qigong?

My teacher reminded me that when we practice qigong, we don't just charge our own internal battery with qi but also become a stronger conduit of energy for healing others. With deep breathing techniques, I was collecting qi in my lower abdomen. The wei qi fields surrounding my body were expanding and becoming more magnetic.

My typically cold hands were becoming warm and tingly. My patients were somehow absorbing the energy that emanated from them. My teacher likened it to osmosis, as energy will always flow from strong to weak. As long as my qi was stronger and cleaner than my patient's qi, I would likely get significantly better healing results.

He also warned me not to treat patients when I was low in energy, because the pathogenic qi from patients' diseases could be absorbed into my body.

I had experienced that. After finishing acupuncture school, I was physically and mentally exhausted and could have benefited from a nice long vacation. However, I was steeped in debt and chose to immediately shift into 'gotta start my practice' mode. A year later, I finally took some time off and traveled home, from Maryland to Western Massachusetts, for some much needed downtime with family and friends.

Much as I wanted to rest, I also wanted to help my dad with his sore, achy feet. They had troubled him for most of his adult life, and nothing he had done for them had helped. He was willing to try acupuncture and I was confident that a few treatments would bring him relief.

I treated my dad each day over the three-day weekend. The first night of my stay, I woke up in the middle of the night to urinate twice. This was odd, because I usually slept straight through the night without waking. I didn't think much about it and assumed it was because I had a beer with a friend earlier that evening. The next night, no beer, but I still woke up three more times to pee. The last night of my stay, I intentionally didn't drink any fluids at all after dinner, but still woke up three times!

In the morning I woke up feeling well rested but was baffled about this nightly urge to urinate.

When I said farewell to my parents, I asked my Dad how his feet were feeling. 'You know, Ted, my feet feel pretty darn good!' he said. 'And I'll tell you what else, I didn't even wake up once to go to the bathroom at night.'

I hadn't known Dad was waking to urinate, so my experience couldn't have been due to preconceived notions.

My classmates in acupuncture school had talked about pathogenic energy, or 'sick qi,' being unintentionally transmitted from patient to healer, but I hadn't fully bought into that theory. Now I believe it. Picking up negative energy really happens.

Qigong practice helped me understand how my body was like a battery bank that could store power. I learned to sense when the energy in my bank was low and when it was abundant.

Qigong provided me with a tool for keeping unwanted energies out, and gave me a larger supply of healing qi to pass on to my patients. I was oozing energy and vitality. My patients noticed the changes, too. They reported better results, and referrals increased.

It was as if all the techniques and special points I had learned in school became secondary in importance compared to the secret magic tool I had in my toolbox. There was simply more voltage behind each needle that I placed into my patients' bodies.

Colleagues and friends from school observed the increase in my patient load and wanted to know what marketing strategy was the key to this success. When I told them that the only thing I changed was adding qigong exercises and meditations to my daily routine, many dismissed the notion. A few followed my example, and it was fun to see their practices grow as well. To this day, when I want to increase my business, I simply practice more qigong to charge my battery and am always amazed at how the phone starts ringing.

Jesus and the Hidden Power

And power came out from him and healed them all
Luke 6:19

My parents, Sunday school teachers, and priest taught me that the miracles Jesus performed were purely acts of God. Jesus would call to God in the form of a prayer, then place his hands on the person, and the healing would then be initiated. It was like magic, and only Jesus and God knew how the action took effect. This may be the case in some healings—however, there is one story in the Bible that demonstrates it wasn't a magic trick activated by a prayer or hands-on touch.

A woman came to Jesus who had been suffering from bleeding for many years. She was exhausted after traveling a long way to see Jesus but knew that simply being near his bountiful energy field would be sufficient enough to heal her. She fought her way through the crowd and reached out to touch the fringe of his robe. By Mosaic Law, women who were 'unclean' were not allowed to touch anyone, as it was believed that anyone they touched would become contaminated, too. Not only did Jesus not become contaminated, but his energy overpowered the affliction. She was immediately healed. Jesus, although not physically touched by the woman, could sense his energy being drawn from his body, as he said to Peter, 'I felt healing power go out from me' (Luke 8:46).

This healing came from the massive amounts of qi that radiated from Jesus' body. There were no prayers spoken prior to this healing, nor did Jesus call to God in any way, nor did he wave his hands on or around the woman's body in any fashion. In fact, Jesus was not even aware of the healing until after it was initiated.

Again, in Luke 6:19, we see a description of Jesus emitting this healing power in significant quantities, suggesting a corporal element to his healings. The crowds, sensing the efficacy of this energy, tried to merely touch Jesus' body, and when they did all were healed.

This 'power' that the Bible mentions again and again in relationship to Jesus and how he healed is an energy that is studied and recognized in Buddhist, Daoist, and Hindu teachings. The Eastern masters knew of this energy, this power, and used ascetic practices such as yoga, qigong, and meditation to cultivate and awaken it in their bodies. These aspirants' main goal was to cultivate powerful energy within to fully awaken all psychic centers for higher consciousness and enlightenment. The healing gifts and supernatural powers that emerged were just a byproduct of the awakening processes.

Pope Paul VI talked specifically about this hidden power and these ascetic practices in his document *Nostra Aetate* (1965):

From ancient times down to the present, there is found among various peoples a certain perception of that **hidden power** *which hovers over the course of things and over the events of human history; at times some indeed have come to the recognition of a Supreme Being, or even of a Father. This perception and recognition penetrates their lives with a profound religious sense.*

Religions, however, that are bound up with an advanced culture have struggled to answer the same questions by means of more refined concepts and a more developed language. **Thus in Hinduism, men contemplate the divine mystery** *and express it through an inexhaustible abundance of myths and through searching philosophical inquiry.* **They seek freedom** *from the anguish of our human condition either* **through ascetical practices or profound meditation** *or a flight to God with love and trust. Again,* **Buddhism, in its various forms,** *realizes the radical insufficiency of this changeable world; it teaches a way by which men, in a devout and confident spirit,* **may be**

221

able either to acquire the state of perfect liberation, or attain, *by their own efforts or through higher help,* **supreme illumination.** *Likewise, other religions found everywhere try to counter the restlessness of the human heart, each in its own manner, by proposing "ways," comprising teachings, rules of life, and sacred rites.* **The Catholic Church rejects nothing that is true and holy in these religions.** *She regards with sincere reverence those ways of conduct and of life,* ***those precepts and teachings which, though differing*** *in many aspects from the ones she holds and sets forth, nonetheless* **often reflect a ray of that Truth which enlightens all men.** *Indeed, she proclaims, and ever must proclaim Christ "the way, the truth, and the life" (John 14:6), in whom men may find the fullness of religious life, in whom God has reconciled all things to Himself.*

We are thus encouraged to ponder the secret teachings of the East on how to perfect the body and soul. This may offer a glimpse of how Jesus wanted us to obtain the miraculous skills and union with God he so often discussed. Jesus emphasized that we're not different from him, that we too are sons and daughters of God, that we possess the Holy Spirit within us, and that we have the power to perform miracles as he did.

For me personally, learning about the secret empowering teachings of the East provided a bridge that brought Jesus' empowering words and inspiration to life.

Paramahansa Yogananda popularized the techniques of Kriya Yoga to millions of westerners through his bestselling book, *Autobiography of a Yogi*. He suggests that many of the world's great masters used these specific teachings. In a separate work titled *The Yoga of Jesus*, he describes how Jesus himself not only traveled to India, but awakened his healing abilities with the meditative techniques of Kriya Yoga.

Today, a number of Christian ashrams are located in Southern India, where the apostle St. Thomas traveled to spread the word of Christ around 50 AD.

Healing Gifts

As my training evolved, I began sharing this knowledge with students. Many potential students inquiring about medical qigong courses are driven by a curiosity about healing. Some tell me reservedly that they possess certain gifts and don't know what to make of them. Usually they don't call them 'gifts,' but phenomena that they cannot explain. A typical opening statement I hear from them is, 'You're probably going to think that I'm crazy, but...'

Frequently, students tell me that they can see things that are not of the earthly realm, like auras around peoples' bodies. Others inform me of premonitions of events that later actually happen.

Still others report being able to easily detect what people are thinking. Some tell me that they're extremely in tune with other people's feelings and emotions, which can be so overwhelming that it leaves them exhausted. Some receive messages in audible voices when nobody is around them. The most interesting part for me is watching my students work on others with medical qigong for the first time. Their excitement as they witness the energetic magic occurring never ceases to gratify me.

One time, I was giving a patient acupuncture treatment and she felt an enormous energy release straight out from the top of her head. It felt wonderful, but scared her because she had never felt anything like this before. I explained to her that she likely experienced an opening of her sixth and seventh chakras and the acupuncture further awakened these psychic centers.

After a few more sessions of acupuncture, she had even more interesting phenomena, such as communication with spirits and angels. I taught her about the relationship between the fifth and sixth chakras and gifts of clairaudience and clairvoyance. At first, she was filled with doubts and fears, but only until she learned more about energy work. She then attained a greater understanding of the energetic and spiritual anatomy of our body and how it can be safely stimulated.

She now has a private practice where she happily practices medical qigong on her clients.

My aunt Chrissy and I had a wonderful conversation during a family gathering at Thanksgiving many years ago. She mentioned casually that she was able to see various 'beautiful' energies in and around peoples' bodies. Once, while standing in line at a bank, she witnessed a young female clerk helping two young men. She saw vortexes of energy spiraling out in front of each of their bodies like cones and eventually merging together in the space in between them. I informed her that what she was likely witnessing was the energy being emitted from their chakras, which naturally swirl outwards from the body. Curiously, I asked her if she had the sense that the men and woman seemed to be flirting with each other. She agreed that they appeared to be flirting. I then asked if the vortexes she witnessed were around heart level, and Chrissy again confirmed with a smile, asking me how I suspected this. I explained that when two people are flirting or in love, their heart chakras become energized. They can expand outward from the body and merge with the other person's chakra. That's often why people who fall in love with each other often 'just know,' because they can feel the spiritual connection without corroborating words or actions.

I was excited to learn that my aunt had such natural psychic gifts and encouraged her to join my classes. Two years later, she began attending. She learned how to better understand and utilize her gifts and she's never looked back.

Today, she treats patients of her own with medical qigong and also offers weekly qigong meditation groups.

I can remember playing a game in elementary school called Doggy Doggy. One student, the dog, would sit up at the front of the room with their back to the class and the chalkboard eraser, the bone, under their seat. While the dog sat with their eyes closed, and with the teacher watching them, one student would steal their bone and sit back down. Then, the dog would turn around and guess which person had taken the bone. I always guessed correctly who stole the bone. Some of my classmates accused me of cheating, but the teacher confirmed that my eyes were indeed closed. At the time I didn't know how I did it, but in retrospect I think I was just tapping into my natural intuitive abilities.

I have come to believe that all human beings have natural healing gifts and energetic, psychic abilities lying dormant within us. In life, many human beings are born with natural gifts to excel in sports, play musical instruments, sing, or display extraordinary mental faculties, with little to no training and at very young ages. Some are born with their extraordinary abilities already awakened, but most have to train to become masters in a particular field. We all have psychic gifts, just as we have mental and physical ones. Our society tends to promote physical and mental gifts that young children possess and direct them into the appropriate schools or training programs. Psychic gifts, however, are not well understood and sometimes even feared. Children are not encouraged, but often taught that these gifts are unusual and should not be spoken of. These latent abilities often lie dormant and are never fully realized.

I wonder where Tiger Woods would be today if his parents took away his golf clubs at age three or if Mozart was denied his piano. Should children's psychic gifts not be valued as much as the gifts that make them athletes, musicians, and artists?

Virtue and Healing

In my earlier years of qigong training, I would often practice healing meditations and breathing exercises that facilitated the release of emotional energies from within my body. The philosophy is that before you practice bringing in ample amounts of qi into the body, you benefit greatly by first ridding yourself of any unclean emotional energy. Energetically, humans store emotions within their internal organs, where they can clog up and cause physical and mental imbalances. For example, years of suppressed anger stored in one's liver can lead to high blood pressure, migraine headaches, menstrual disharmony, or digestive issues.

Cultivating healing qi into the liver before first purging this stagnation could actually create more health issues. Think of it like firing up a wood stove in the wintertime. If used correctly, a wood stove can safely provide heat to a home throughout the cold winter months. However, if the creosote is not cleaned out of the chimney each season, you could end up with a dangerous and costly house fire. Emotions are to our body as creosote is to a chimney. Both are natural and harmless in manageable amounts, but if either builds up excessively, without regular cleanup, you could create unwanted side effects.

Personally, I carried many toxic emotions for several years. It wasn't until I started ridding myself of the excess baggage that I recognized how much my emotions weighed on me and affected my health. At times during my initial training, I would randomly cry, which is something I rarely do. I didn't necessarily feel sad when it happened. The tears that flowed felt more like a healthy release of old garbage from my body.

Although I still feel and express emotions daily, I don't feel as if they have any negative impact on me. Being able to watch my emotions and control them has allowed me to be a better person and a better healer. It's as if my emotions were a hindrance to my overall happiness and health. Releasing some of them felt quite revitalizing.

When I train students how to use medical qigong in my annual certification classes, the entire first week of training focuses on self-care. In other words, students focus on healing themselves before ever laying a hand on healing another. Healers must radiate health from within before they can effectively heal others. I teach them how to cultivate clean energy from the environment, store it into their body, and then eventually release it to others for healing. Most importantly, I teach them first how to get rid of their own unclean energies.

A few years back, I had an enthusiastic student named Michael, who practiced the qigong cultivating exercises and meditations diligently. After the first week of training, he went home and practiced every day. After a couple of months, he contacted me explaining that he was feeling great and had noticed various improvements in his health. However, he also told me that he was feeling various uncharacteristic emotions arising and noticed he was occasionally being a 'jerk' to his family and friends. Having a sense about the situation, I asked him which exercises and meditations he had been performing each day. He informed me that he was doing mostly cultivation, but none of the detoxification exercises.

I then reminded him that cultivating energy is like consuming water. Most would not consider drinking water from a dirty glass. Nor would you benefit from bringing clean energy into an unclean body. Although it's exciting to feel the immediate benefits of increased energy in the body from qigong practices, if one doesn't purge their excess emotions first, any subsequent meditations can be potentially unsafe.

One must rid the excess emotional energies first in order to avoid potentially firing up old patterns of anger or anxiety.

Once Michael incorporated the emotional detoxification exercises into his daily routine, his irritability vanished and he continued on, healing himself and others with great success down the road.

It is essential that anyone delving deeply into spiritual practices of meditation, yoga, and qigong seek a qualified teacher or spiritual guide. Anything you do in life has potential dangers if not practiced correctly. From crossing the road to riding a bike to eating food or taking prescription medications, everything comes with directions. If directions are not followed, then any of our actions can potentially be unsafe. Many feel that ascetic disciplines like qigong and meditation are dangerous to practice. However, if performed properly, under the correct guidance, these rituals are not only safe but extremely life-giving. Purging and purifying your emotions as you progress along a focused spiritual quest is absolutely vital.

Negative emotions are a deterrent in healing oneself and others, but the specific cultivation of positive emotions (virtues) has an immense power in healing. It's no surprise that some of the most effective healers are also virtuous in nature. In some translations of Jesus' healing the bleeding woman in the Bible, the word 'virtue' is used in describing the energy that flowed from his body to cure her (Luke 8:45). Jesus healed not only through the word of God and the laying on of hands, but also by the sheer virtue that he radiated outwards.

By cultivating the virtues of love, faith, trust, willpower, fearlessness, and compassion all humans can display this ability as well. This further indicates that Jesus' power to heal was not just a magical gift from God, but from the energy and virtue he cultivated throughout his lifetime.

Spiritual Exercise:
Deep Breathing for Increased Energy and Health

Long, slow, and deep breathing helps to increase healing qi energy in the body. Deep breathing also helps to lower blood pressure, improves digestion and peristalsis, decreases anxiety and depression, and promotes a tranquil state of mind. Long breaths are associated with a long life. Shallow breathing is associated with a weak heart and shorter life.

> Start by timing your breath for 60 seconds. One inhalation and one exhalation equals one breath. Breathe naturally and record your total breaths for 60 seconds, then write down this number.

> Next, practice breathing slowly and deeply in and out through your nose. Breathe naturally, without forcing the breath, but use your intention to slowly increase the depth of your breath as time passes. Eventually your diaphragm muscle will begin loosening and your breath will become smoother, deeper, and longer. Listen to your body, and watch for warm sensations, tingling, and heaviness. These are signs that qi is increasing in your body.

> Continue this exercise for several minutes per day. After one month of practice you should easily be able to lower your breathing to one or two deep breaths per minute, which is extremely beneficial to your health on all levels.

Chapter Fifteen:
Fasting on Fridays

When I was young altar boy serving mass every Sunday at St Catherine's Church, my faith in Jesus and the Catholic Church grew. I came to believe that Catholicism was the one true path to God and heaven. I respected other people's belief systems but felt that my path was the best way and right way.

In college, I met friends who held a weekly Bible study and invited me to join. I went to a couple of meetings and enjoyed discussing the sacred word. After some time, however, I pondered whether these visits would interfere with my Catholic faith. The following Sunday, I spoke with the priest at the Catholic Church on campus after mass.

For forty days, being tempted by the devil.
And he ate nothing during those days.

Luke 4:2

The priest advised me gently to avoid such Bible studies because only priests were to interpret the word of the God.

I told my friends politely that I would no longer take part in their Bible study group. I felt comfortable with my decision and knew that it was the right thing to do.

Just a few short years later, I began suffering with the various health maladies that I've described earlier in this book and sought Eastern methods of healing. My openness to try methods such as acupuncture and qigong created a bridge that allowed me to gently learn about Eastern religions and their paths to enlightenment. Since the theories of Eastern medicine correlated so closely with their religion and spiritual pursuits, I didn't view my studies as being in conflict with my Catholic faith. However, as I delved deeper into Eastern thought and began resonating with their philosophies on medicine, spirituality, and the specific link between the two, I developed a new perspective and appreciation. I realized there might be more than one path to God and heaven.

Since my early twenties, I've become much more open to listening to others' opinions about religion and spirituality. In fact, I welcome spiritual discussions with people of all faiths, even atheists. Instead of immediately closing my mind off to opposing belief systems, I listen and try to understand other viewpoints. I find it interesting to hear other peoples' views about the bigger questions in life.

By embracing ideas from others, I learn more about my own faith.

When I met with Brother Seif, we spoke for hours about many different spiritual topics. He told me that ex-Catholics are one of the biggest and fastest-growing 'religions' in the world today. When speaking with many ex-Catholics, I always asked why they turned away from the Church, something I once found difficult to understand. To me, the Catholic faith was the true path to God and enlightenment. How could someone turn away from it?

More times than not, these people were repelled by the man-made rules that they believed had nothing to do with Jesus Christ's original teachings. They felt that the priests and nuns put too much emphasis on sin and punishment instead of the inspirational aspects of Jesus' teachings.

One friend thought the rule that you had to fast on Fridays during Lent was nonsensical. At the time, it was said that eating meat on Lenten Fridays was a mortal sin for which you would be sent to hell. How many poor saps, he wondered, were rotting in hell because they had accidentally eaten a Big Mac on the wrong date?

Although I too questioned many principles taught to me during my Catholic upbringing, I tried to seek the truth that lay within these teachings before jumping ship.

There is one aspect of my early Christian tutelage that I have never questioned for a second: the existence of a truly divine being named Jesus Christ who walked the earth and performed miracles nearly two thousand years ago. Jesus never self-promoted, never wrote a book, never made a movie, nor did he have a YouTube channel (so far as I know) to spread his word. Aside from the Shroud of Turin, the man never even had a self-portrait or photo taken of himself. I figure that if we're still talking about a man over two thousand years later, he must have been something extra special. If all the claims of his miraculous abilities were fabricated, his story would have disintegrated long ago. Even many of today's most heroic and celebrated individuals are forgotten soon after their prominence diminishes.

When I began my intensive studies in Eastern religions, I noticed similarities between the rules of the Catholic Church and those from our friends in the Far East. For example, the process of fasting seems to be a cornerstone in most major religions and is used as a tool to purify the body, mind, and spirit. However, in Eastern religions fasting doesn't serve as punishment or to remind us of the suffering that our deities had to endure. Instead, it's used to *eliminate* human suffering.

You may wonder how starving oneself for days or weeks on end could create happiness or pleasure. However, there are many extraordinary health benefits to fasting and tens of thousands practice this art every year without any ill effects.

Fasting is one of the oldest and most effective forms of healing known to mankind. Even animals instinctively stop eating food when they are sick to restore their body back to health. Humans seem to have lost the natural fasting instinct, because they eat more when they're sick.

When performing a water fast for more than twenty-four hours, your body sends a signal to the digestive system that the fuel sources have been cut off. The body then shifts all its enzymatic energy towards finding other energy sources in order to survive. The body doesn't just use fat and muscle reserves for energy until you starve to death. It will only burn a limited amount of lean muscle tissue. Then it searches for fuel from non-protein sources: viruses, bacteria, yeast, parasites, degenerative tissues, calcium deposits, arterial plaque, and cancers. Fasting is one of the best ways to clean up and detoxify the body of all the unwanted junk that so often creates disease.

Fasting and other methods of detoxification have been effective tools to restore my own body's health after dietary abuse. It got rid of yeasts, parasites, heavy metals, and other toxins, and hundreds of gallstones. It increased my energy, restored most of my digestive functioning, and improved my immune system dramatically.

Studies show that fasting helps normalize insulin sensitivity, which could reduce the risk of diseases like diabetes, obesity, and cancer. Fasting has also been shown to stimulate the production of human growth hormone (HGH), which naturally declines as we age—an important benefit, because low levels correlate with many diseases. Increased production of HGH can increase lean muscle mass, burn fat, and increase your life span. Fasting lowers bad cholesterol and triglycerides, which makes for a healthy heart. Studies also suggest that, while fasting, the body experiences beneficial changes in several genes and molecules that relate to longevity and protection against disease.

Much like the process of medical qigong for inducing the release of old emotions and traumatic memories that get stored in the body and cause disease, fasting purges unwanted emotional energies. Many who fast for more than seven days report painful memories surfacing, followed by calm and peace after the fast.

Spiritually speaking, fasting is right up there with prayer and meditation for establishing a stronger connection to God and the spiritual life. As Mahatma Ghandi once said: 'Fasting will bring spiritual rebirth to those of you who cleanse and purify your bodies. The light of the world will illuminate within you when you fast and purify yourself. What the eyes are for the outer world, fasts are for the inner.'

Fasting is like hitting CTRL-ALT-DEL on your computer. Whenever your computer stops working or slows, you hit these buttons to restart it, and often once you do the problem has gone. Fasting is like a reset button for your body that erases the deleterious actions from many years of abuse. Spiritually speaking, fasting erases sin and karma and brings us more in alignment with our divine nature. Fasting is a means to cleanse the physical body, the mind, and the soul.

Christians have a long history of fasting. Jesus fasted frequently for up to forty days and encouraged us to fast as well.

Jesus had to work to prepare his body to be synchronized with God's way. He escaped to the desert for extended periods to fast and meditate. This allowed him to maintain his health, energy levels, and abilities to perform supernatural feats.

Although it seems difficult to believe, those who fast for seven or more days often reach a point of increased energy. Jesus needed to recuperate to restore his healing power again and again. This demonstrates that Jesus' talents were not just God-given but required consistent recharging.

St. Augustine (354-430 AD) said, 'Fasting purifies the soul. It uplifts the mind, and brings the body into subjection to the spirit. It makes the heart contrite and humble, scatters the clouds of desire, puts out the flames of lust and enkindles the true light of chastity.'

For me, looking outside the Catholic 'box' and seeing how other religions use fasting to rejuvenate the body and soul gave me a new perspective. It also reinforced the notion of the connection between the health of the body and that of the soul.

Although in Christian culture, fasting is practiced regularly, the Bible gives little explanation on how to perform it safely and effectively. Through Eastern medicine, I came to understand the process. Many books about fasting exist, but I suggest you start fasting under the supervision of a skilled teacher.

The body obviously doesn't just require food to survive. It needs energy, and it can get energy from sources other than food. This is where prana and qi come into play. Qi is obtained mostly from the air that we breathe. When one trains the body in ascetic practices such as yoga, meditation, qigong, and fasting, it is possible to attain energy for daily bodily functions.

I'll never forget the first time I attempted a seven-day water-only fast.

The first day was fine. 'No problem,' I thought. However, when the twenty-fourth hour struck, my body shifted into detox mode and I grew tired, achy, and weak, feeling as if I had a hangover. I wasn't terribly hungry, I just felt like poisons were seeping into my bloodstream.

I couldn't take it. I gave up and ate. Within minutes my body ceased cleansing, and soon after I felt almost back to normal.

Sometimes, when it comes to your health, it's not about things *to do* or *to take* to bring balance but what to avoid or stop. The organs in your body need rest and cleaning from time to time. Could you imagine not getting your oil filter in your car replaced? The filters in your body cannot be replaced, but they can and should be cleaned out regularly. Fasting is an excellent method. People often ask me about how to lose weight, what foods to eat and what diet to follow. I tell them what they could be avoiding and encourage them to cleanse the liver, our main fat burning organ.

The main motive for fasting is often spiritual. Fasting, much like meditation, allows the body to shift its energy from external stimuli to our inner soul. Many holy persons and spiritual aspirants have gained greater insight and intuition through the fasting process.

Although it's difficult grasp how someone can go without food for twenty, thirty, or even forty days at a time, and some scientists claim you would die after two weeks without food, evidence suggests that it works.

My friend Loren Lockman runs the successful Tanglewood Wellness Center, where he and his staff lead supervised water fasts. He usually suggests a minimum of twenty days of fasting on only water. Many of his regular clients fast for much longer than that, up to forty or more days, much like Jesus did. Not only do his clients survive from these fasts, but you can view the dozens of video testimonials online from his clients who speak in detail of how the fasts improved their condition, helping with Lyme's disease, chronic pain, acne, thyroid issues, psoriasis, cancer, joint pain, candida and other fungal issues, chronic fatigue syndrome, fibromyalgia, Epstein-Barr syndrome, rheumatoid arthritis, chronic depression, and anxiety. Many report healing decades-long relationship issues with family and friends. Others report a profound feeling of peace and a stronger connection to God.

Blessed Alexandrina Da Costa (1904-1955) spent the last thirteen years of her life fasting, living only on the Holy Eucharist that she received daily. After many mocked her and claimed she was a liar, strict medical supervision certified her fast was legitimate.

Prahlad Jani, a Hindu holy man in India, had a religious experience when he was eleven years old and since that time has not consumed food or water. He is now in his seventies and in excellent health. He has gone through extensive medical supervision, both in 2003 and in 2010, which both confirmed that he didn't eat or drink. Blood tests taken at the end of the fasting periods came back completely normal. The physicians who monitored him stated that he was in better health than most people half his age.

Jesus told us that man 'cannot live on bread alone,' (Matthew 4:4) and encouraged others to fast as well (Matthew 6:16-18). When Jesus made this statement, I feel he was referring to the universal energy of qi that is abundant in our world and available to everyone.

Celibate or Celebrate?

As a senior in high school, I served my last year as an altar boy. I drove down to St. Catherine's and arrived about twenty minutes early to perform my pre-mass chores as one of five altar boys. I went into the sacristy and put on my white cassock and red cape. Then I lit the candles on the altar and prepared the water and wine for mass. My duties gave me a sense of importance.

As I walked back into the sacristy from the altar, I heard the other altar boys, all good friends, laughing. When I asked them what was so funny, they told me a joke that is still one of my favorites to this day:

'A young Catholic monk arrives at the monastery and is assigned to help the other monks in copying the old laws of the church by hand. He notices that the old monks are copying from copies and not the original manuscript. As the new monk explains this to the head monk, citing the importance of preciseness, the head monk agrees. The head monk then goes down into the dark basement several stories below the monastery where the original manuscripts are held in a vault. Hours go by and nobody sees the head monk. So, the young monk, worried, goes down to look for him. He finds him banging his head against the wall, his forehead bloodied and bruised, wailing.

"We missed the R! We missed the R!"

The young monk asks what was wrong. The head monk, with tears in his eyes, replies, "The word is *celebrate*, not *celibate*!!'"

Although this was just a funny joke, it brings up the question of celibacy and what it actually provides for a spiritual aspirant. Members of the church hierarchy are usually forbidden to marry and must refrain from sex. I know of many ex-Catholics and current Catholics who feel that this rule should be changed. Many feel that sex is an instinctive need and that it's unnatural to suppress its great power. One friend told me that he thought it was just another form of anguish that priests had to endure, in the same way that Jesus had to endure long periods without food and water in the desert. I too have often wondered how priests and nuns were able to refrain from sex without driving themselves crazy and often speculated as to how celibacy could benefit someone both physically and spiritually.

Sex is a driving force of nature. The powerful biological urge in both humans and animals to procreate could be the most potent energy source that our bodies possess. As I gained greater insights into how sexual energy was viewed in Chinese medicine, I developed a new perspective about celibacy. The masters from the East understood that sexual energy was just that, a very powerful energy, difficult to tame. However, they learned that through various practices, this energy could be harnessed, diverted, and cultivated for many purposes.

The Chinese believe that qi is what promotes life in all living things and that the loss of body fluids leads to the loss of qi. Semen is believed to contain the most concentrated amounts of qi (in the form of *jing qi*) in the body, and when expended too often, it could lead to a shortened life and poor health. The Chinese thus developed various 'bedroom arts,' which allowed both man and woman to enjoy heightened and sustained states of 'activity' without depleting this precious jing qi prematurely.

Ancient Chinese martial artists purposely avoided sexual activities for weeks and months before a battle or athletic event in order to increase their vigor and aggressiveness. I certainly would hate to fight a man who's refrained from sex for several months. That would be like confronting a tiger that's been denied meat for weeks.

The practice of sexual abstinence has made its way to the West, and many boxers and MMA fighters adhere to it before big fights, including Manny Pacquiao, Rocky Marciano and Travis Boehm. Fighters believe this increases their endurance, stamina, and fierceness in the ring. I once asked one of my patients, a retired boxing coach who had worked with well-known boxers, including Mohamed Ali, if the 'avoiding sex before a big fight' legend was true. He confirmed it was: Ali himself followed it.

By controlling sexual energy, you can learn to awaken the vast spiritual anatomy within the body. This helps your pursuit of enlightenment and good health. Jing qi resides mostly in the lower chakras.

Every person is born with a certain amount of jing qi, which represents our health, vitality, and overall strength and constitution. By learning preservation and cultivation techniques taught by the masters of the East, we can awaken the higher psychic centers and attain union with God.

I asked Brother Seif, who was well versed in Chinese medicine and meditation, if he practiced the 'small circulation' meditation. One of the most commonly taught meditations in qigong, it circulates sexual energy from the reproductive organs upwards through the body in order to promote health and awaken the spiritual mind. This also serves to tame intense sexual urges by drawing jing qi up through the body.

He smiled sheepishly. 'Why yes. It saved my life!'

The reality is that sexual energy is just that, energy. Energy can be channeled and used as we wish on this earthly realm, for fun, for health, for athletic endeavors, or for spiritual enlightenment. We have free will to use our sexual energy as we please. Yet Eastern philosophy shows that a holy life needs to be balanced by living in accordance with the healthy way. Our sexual desires are natural, but with practice, they can be focused towards spiritual growth.

I don't believe that fasting and celibacy are evil forms of torture, but ways to possibly enrich our lives and nourish our souls.

Confession Dilemma

In my early twenties, just before I began my tutelage in Chinese medicine, I was dating a girl who was also Catholic. I would define her as a reluctant Catholic. We went to church together on Sundays, but she insisted to going to a mass where the sermon was positive, not full of 'gloom and doom.' I too wanted Sunday sermons to inspire me, so we found a good church in town with a progressive pastor.

One time, I suggested to her that we go to confession so we could 'absolve' our sins. She gave me a look of disgust and retorted that she didn't need a priest to forgive her sins. If and when she felt the need to confess, she felt comfortable to talk directly to Jesus. I saw her point. When I went to confession alone that weekend, I thought about her words more than the actual transgressions that I was atoning for.

After pondering this notion many times over the years, I have come to agree with her viewpoint. Why do we have to go through the church and a priest to have our sins forgiven? If we are to develop a relationship with Jesus through prayer, why can't we just ask him for forgiveness directly? I wondered if Jesus ever actually told us that we were to go through one of his disciples, in the form of Church hierarchy, to ask for forgiveness. Jesus never mentioned any concept of confession that I knew of and he actually encouraged us all to forgive each other for our actions.

It made sense to me, since sin is born from man, that man should likely clean up his own mess.

Sin is not born in heaven, with Jesus or of God; men on earth create it. Maybe God wanted us to forgive each other rather than asking someone who never stopped loving us in the first place. To forgive means to stop feeling angry. I no longer believe that God is an angry and jealous God who will turn against me and destroy me from the face of the earth (Deuteronomy 6:15).

Jesus also said that the way to be forgiven is to first forgive others. Time and time again, Jesus preached and displayed forgiveness, not anger, as when he said, 'Do not judge, and you will not be judged. Do not condemn, and you will not be condemned. Forgive, and you will be forgiven' (Luke 6:37).

Also, 'Be kind and compassionate to one another, forgiving each other, just as in Christ God forgave you' (Ephesians 4:32).

Although I've seen many a Catholic turn away from Christianity because of perceived 'silly rules,' my faith only increased. Instead of getting rid of something essential because of something inessential, I made an effort to understand the hows and whys of these rules. As a youth, I had struggled to understand the purpose of some rules, but studying the tenets of other religions gave me new perspectives on Jesus' teachings.

Then I wondered: when the man-made Catholic Church and its rules were established, how many of Jesus' true teachings made it through the filtering process?

The continual reform of the Church and the constant changing of rules and regulations show that we may still have more to learn about the life and teachings of Jesus Christ.

For me, this may have been the greatest gift of healing. Learning Eastern medicine has facilitated my personal healing, and understanding the tenets of other religions has given me a deeper understanding of my own faith.

I find it sad how many people turn away from Christianity because of man-made rules. Jesus' true teaching can relieve humans of much suffering.

Chapter Sixteen:
The Journey Ahead

My dad grimaced with his eyes half closed as I hovered my right palm over and around his head. He had been diagnosed with minor skin cancer spots on his face, and I wanted to discover what they felt like energetically.

The year was 2010. Over the years, my father had become comfortable with me administering acupuncture to him and had actually began to enjoy the relaxing sensations. Yet this would be the first time I ever treated him with medical qigong. He knew that I incorporated more and more qigong into my practice, and that I was training medical doctors, nurses, massage therapists, and acupuncturists in this ancient healing art. My mother had begun practicing the qigong med-

May your Kingdom come soon.
May your will be done on earth,
as it is in heaven.

Matthew 6:10

itations as well. I had given her a DVD I had created, a guided qigong session, and she did it regularly. She also benefited from the medical qigong treatments that I gave her. Finally, Dad's curiosity won and he wanted to try it himself.

He lay back in his chair in the same living room where I had first introduced Chinese medicine to him nearly fifteen years before. I inserted needles in his feet and hands to stimulate the qi and witnessed him slowly drift into a more quiescent state. I then prepared myself to perform medical qigong on him.

As I worked my way up to his head and began scanning, he told me that he was getting odd sensations, but assured me he they weren't uncomfortable. After a few more minutes, his demeanor turned from calm to apprehensive. Even though I was sure I hadn't done anything to cause concern, Dad lacked full faith in the process of medical qigong. I had learned over the years that the less anxiety, discomfort, or fear the patient feels, the better. So I stopped the qigong and simply finished the session with acupressure and acupuncture. I hoped that someday I would inspire him to try it again.

While I was writing this book in 2016, Dad grew curious about the project and asked if he could read the draft. After reading it, he became so inspired by the concept of energy medicine he asked once again for a medical qigong treatment. This time, he was far less hesitant. We moved from the TV room to the living room, where I had my massage table set up and would be free of distractions. I played Indian flute music from my iPhone and laid him down on the table to get comfortable.

My dad was dealing with severe fatigue, high blood pressure, edema in his legs, and pain in his knees. Above all, he was struggling with frustration over a personal issue that he was dealing with. The anger was consuming his thoughts so much that Mom and Dad both considered it a serious problem. I explained to him that emotions are just energy and can be dispersed like water on a hot stove. I scanned his internal organs and noticed a significant amount of stagnation in his liver. This correlated with his current symptoms of fatigue, irritability, high blood pressure, and joint pain, all liver qi stagnation symptoms according to TCM theory.

I wanted to clear the stagnation using medical qigong techniques, and at the same time let Dad truly feel the qi moving in his body as I manipulated it. So, I decided to apply more advanced qigong methods that would create stronger vibrations that he might notice more significantly.

I used projected healing sounds to disperse the stuck energy in his liver. Healing sounds have been used for centuries in many cultures and are excellent at breaking up stagnant energy of all kinds. Some singers can hit such high notes that they break glass—evidence of the power and energy of sound.

In this case, rather than shattering windows, these gentle sounds would help to promote well being in my dad.

I stood over my dad as he lay relaxed on the table and blew the shuuu (pronounced 'shoe') sound into his body, directing it towards his liver, without physically touching him at all. After about five to ten breaths, I once again saw the curious look on his face emerge, this time minus the fear. I asked him how he was doing and he told me that he felt energy moving throughout his body, from his legs all the way up to his head. He found the experience strange but not uncomfortable. I continued to move and disperse the stagnation out of his body for several minutes.

He was feeling lighter, as if his body was about to float off the table. Cautiously astonished, he said, 'Ted, this stuff is amazing!'—exactly the same words he had used twenty years before when I first introduced him to Eastern medicine.

A week later he called to tell me that he drove up to the White Mountains in New Hampshire to go hiking with my mom for a couple of days. This was remarkable, because in recent months his fatigue had been so severe he was barely able to take his routine daily walk around the block. He also told me his joint pain was reduced, blood pressure was down, and that he felt much more peaceful in nature. He thanked me repeatedly. Making my dad feel better warmed my heart.

Three months later, I came back home to give a lecture on acupuncture at my Alma Mata, UMass Amherst, and saw my parents once again. I noticed that Dad wasn't complaining about the issue that had caused him so much anger. I brought the topic up casually and asked if it was still bothering him. He thought about it for a minute and matter-of-factly said no. Mom and Dad both felt that his irritability had subsided sometime in the summer shortly after I had treated him with medical qigong.

Over the years, I've had the great honor of introducing many to the powerful healing benefits of medical qigong through my certification classes, including conventional medical practitioners as well as students and masters of the 'healing arts.' It excites me to see how more and more people are opening up to medical qigong as an effective, safe, and low-cost therapy that can treat many diseases. In 2015, I received an email from a Catholic priest who had an intense interest in Chinese Energetic Medicine. Soon after, he joined my classes, and he has just recently finished his second year of training and is certified as a medical qigong therapist. He now offers free medical qigong healing sessions to his parishioners after Sunday mass, garnering great interest within the congregation and helping many.

It doesn't matter if you are black or white, Christian or Muslim, American or Russian, poor or rich, sinner or saint. It also doesn't matter where you go to Church or what political stance you take. We all are children of God and possess the same spiritual anatomy.

The source of this anatomy is our God-given eternal soul that can be easily aroused with simple ageless tools. Meditation, yoga, qigong, fasting, and other ascetic practices are the most effective means to kindle the fire of our soul. Through stillness one can awaken the deepest potential of their being. As Jesus said, 'Be still and know that I am God' (Psalm 46:10).

My personal journey led me to the heartland of healing and spirituality as I learned techniques from Daoist, Hindu, and Buddhist origins. I look forward to keeping an open mind and learning more about the various cultures of the world and how they utilize healing knowledge. Maybe I will learn about how Muslims view healing. Sufism and Native American traditions have strong beliefs towards healing and spirituality. I could embrace Jewish teachings on healing as well. Remember, Jesus was a Jew.

The discoveries I've made in seeing various Catholics teaching and practicing Eastern medicine like acupuncture and qigong inspire me. To my great pleasure, I recently learned that even the current Pope Francis has indulged in Chinese medicine to successfully treat several severe health issues.

As reported by TAO magazine (Argentina) in its October 2013 issue, Pope Francis, formerly Cardinal Jorge Bergoglio, began receiving treatments from an Eastern physician. Daoist monk Dr. Liu Ming began treating Pope Francis in 2004 for a heart condition, which his doctors said required surgery. Dr. Liu Ming treated him in three sessions per week at the cathedral where Cardinal Jorge resided. At the time, the cardinal suffered with lung, liver, and heart problems. He had taken many medications before beginning Chinese medical treatments. Within three years, he was off all his medications and saw a dramatic improvement in his health and well-being.

He had first learned of Dr. Liu Ming through one of the priests at the cathedral who had also been a beneficiary of his healing gifts. In 2013, Pope Francis contacted Dr. Liu Ming and asked him if he would stop by the Vatican while on his journey to China, and the physician agreed.

It's exciting to see so many Christians at all levels of the Catholic Church opening up to witness the many wonderful benefits of Eastern medicine. It is also no surprise that a progressive Pope Francis has openly embraced knowledge from other religions to raise his vibrational energy. My hope is that Pope Francis and others within the hierarchy of the Catholic Church will implement healing practices into Christian congregations throughout the world. I support Brother Seif's wish to make healing the eighth sacrament and promote what may have been Jesus' main inspiration to us.

We live in a world that's desperate for safe, effective, low-cost forms of healing the body. In the U.S. we spend more money on healthcare than anywhere else in the entire world. Examining basic economic theories of cost-benefit analysis and return on investment, we should be the healthiest country in the entire world.

However, we are one of the sickest.

We're among the world *leaders* in most major chronic degenerative diseases, including obesity, heart disease, arthritis, back pain, anxiety, and cancer. One could make a case that we're also becoming one of the most spiritually lacking people as well.

It often seems that Jesus Christ is most frequently spoken of when people are cursing his name. Christmas has become more about Santa Claus and Black Friday than of celebrating Jesus Christ's arrival into the world. Somehow it's even become politically incorrect to say 'Merry Christmas' during the most sacred time for Christians. I will never forget Father O'Connor's passionate sermon each year on Christmas day. He would always ask the congregation, 'What would you actually do if Jesus Christ showed up on your doorstep, in his sandals and modest attire, during your holiday party? Would you let him in?'

Friends, we have the greatest Christmas gift in the world inside our own body just waiting to be unwrapped. We can attain greater levels of peace, prosperity, happiness and well-being than we could ever imagine. We all have the same potential as Jesus Christ residing within our soul just waiting to be awakened. You don't have to live in a monastery or retreat to the mountains for years at a time and meditate in a cave to begin this process. All you need to do is take a few minutes each day, close your eyes, quiet your mind and breathe.

I wake each day with the enthusiasm of a kid on Christmas morning waiting to unwrap his gifts. That gift is the unlimited potential and light of my God-given soul. The only things that separates me from this potential is the 'wrapping paper' that is my ego. When we dissolve the thick turbid layers of negative thoughts, emotions, and disease, we can attain eternal peace and happiness.

Imagine the possibilities if we could spread the universal law of love and healing throughout the world, just as all major religions preach. Love is light and heals all. Imagine a world today in which we could all exude the same healing energy and love as Jesus Christ. That's a world I'd like to live in. That is the 'heaven on earth' that Jesus spoke of so many times in the Bible.

I believe that the second coming of Jesus will arrive soon. However, I believe that Jesus may not take individual human form as many might expect. I believe he's patiently waiting for all of us to awaken the 'Christ' within our own soul. He came once to show us how it was done, but we have not utilized the teachings yet. This is what I believe the 'second coming of Christ' truly represents.

Whenever I walk into Church and see Jesus hanging from the cross, I feel such humility at the thought of a man who suffered beyond imagination for us. Let's take Jesus down from the cross and begin *his* healing process. Let's bring Jesus back into our hearts and souls by living out his true teachings of love, light, and heaven on earth, just as he did when he lived on this earth.

It was such a thrill for me to heal someone for the first time when I treated my father for his shoulder pain. Alleviating suffering for people is something I do every day.

The side effects of my treatments are increased energy levels, better mood, better digestion, improved sleeping, and reduced physical pain. People walk into my office each week in pain and walk out with a smile on their face, amazed that the pain has vanished. I lay my hands on people each day in efforts to alleviate human suffering just as Jesus did two thousand years ago.

Thousands of others do the same, and we *all* possess this special skill. I encourage the world to embrace the techniques written about in this work and convey them throughout society.

I hope to someday walk into Church on Sunday morning and witness a twenty-minute meditation as part of the service. I'd love to see healing services offered to those in need after mass just as my friend and student Father Bill Sloane does at his church. I'd love to see yoga and qigong exercises taught to Christians around the world so their bodies can become true temples for their eternal souls.

Sometimes the trial and tribulations of life can get us down. When I was feeling beaten down by my health issues during the most difficult period of my life, I could have easily lost faith. I could have cursed God and questioned why he did this to me. I could have turned from God in disgust because he wasn't helping me or answering my prayers. But the reality is that if I had just opened my eyes, I would have realized that he was right there the whole time holding my hand. He was guiding me towards greater levels of health and happiness that surpassed even my utmost dreams. This reminded me that beautiful flowers always blossom after long, cold, and dismal winters, and so too can our soul flourish after trauma and suffering.

I do not wish to relive the challenges I endured in my early adulthood. But I realize that these hardships led me to Chinese medicine and Eastern philosophy, which ended up being the greatest blessing in my life. By learning Eastern medicine, I not only learned to restore my health but grew a career out of helping others. There is no greater feeling than to rid someone of pain and suffering that you too have endured.

Mostly, however, by learning about Eastern philosophy I developed a greater relationship with God and an enhanced understanding of Jesus' life and teachings. Now, when I read the Bible, I am no longer confused by parables, omissions, and difficult to comprehend verses. I look at Jesus' words with new inspiration and meaning.

I understand what Jesus meant when he said that God lies within us.

He encouraged us to embrace this wonderful healing power and 'let your light shine before others' (Matthew 5:16).

I've come to develop a completely different appreciation of the practices of fasting, celibacy, and meditation.

When I hear or read about the trendy term 'body, mind, and spirit,' I have a sound comprehension of what this means.

I used to read verses about the 'power' and 'virtue' that was emitted from Jesus when he healed others and scratched my head. Now, I understand what this power is, how Jesus used it, and mostly, how I too can cultivate it within myself.

I now understand why so many Catholics have turned away from the Church, and sometimes from Christianity altogether. When a holy text contains so many instructions yet so few tools, it's easy to see how one could get confused and frustrated.

I appreciate verses where Jesus encourages us to exude virtue and temper emotions of anger, fear, and anxiety. I now have specific tools to attain these principles in my life.

The Bible vaguely states that Jesus grew in wisdom and in stature with God and man. I now have an idea of where he gained this wisdom and exactly how he did so.

I believe that Jesus Christ is the most influential, most loved, most hated, most worshipped, most cursed, and most misunderstood man ever to walk the face of the earth.

I hope this work inspires others to become closer to God and to Jesus. I think the true spiritual path brings enormous health, joy, love, and success into all aspects of our lives. Isn't this what we all seek?

Have faith and believe in Jesus Christ's words when he was asked about the Kingdom of heaven: 'Neither shall they say, Lo, it is here! Or lo, it is there! For, behold, the kingdom of God is within you' (Luke 17:21).

We now have tools and knowledge to attain our own Godliness. 'I have said, Ye *are* Gods; and all of you *are* children of the most High' (Psalm 82:6).

BIBLIOGRAPHY

Benson, Herbert, Lehmann, John W., Malhotra, M.S., Goldman, Ralph F., Hopkins, Jeffrey, Epstein, Mark D., *Body Temperature Changes During the Practice of g Tum-mo yoga*, Harvard Medical School, Beth Israel Hospital, Boston, Massachusetts, 1982.

Csikszentmihalyi, Mihaly, *Flow: The Psychology of Optimal Experience*, Harper and Row, 1990.

Danaos, Kosta, *The Magus of Java: Teachings of an Authentic Taoist Immortal*, Inner Traditions, 2000.

Espinoza, Jose, *Why Don't Boxers Have Sex Before a Fight?*, September 29th, 2010, http://www.askmen.com/dating/love_tip/538_sex-training.html

Franciscan Friars of the Immaculate, *Padre Pio: The Wonder Worker*, Ignatius Press, 1999.

Hagelin JS; Orme-Johnson DW; Rainforth M; Cavanaugh K; Alexander CN; Shatkin SF; Davies JL; Hughs AO; Ross E; *"Effects of Group Practice of the Transcendental Meditation Program on Preventing Violent Crime in Washington, D.C.: Results of the National Demonstration Project, June--July 1993"*, D.C.Institute of Science, Technology and Public Policy Technical Report 94:1, 1994. Social Indicators Research (vol 47 issue 2: 153-201, 1999)

Hebert S. M., Father Alfred J., *Saints Who Raised the Dead*, Tan Books, 2004.

Johnson, Dr. Jerry Alan, *Chinese Medical Qigong Therapy: A Comprehensive Clinical Text*, International Institute of Medical Qigong, 2000.

Julian of Norwich, Hudleston, Roger, *Revelations of Divine Love*, Dover Publications, 2006.

King James Version Bible, STANDARD EDITION, Copyright 2013 Christian Art Publishers, PO BOX 1599 , Vareeniging 1930 RSA

Lutz, Antoine, Lewis, Julie, Johnstone, Tom, Davidson, Richard J., *Regulation of Neural Circuitry of Emotion by Compassion Meditation: Effects of Medicine Expertise*, March 26th, 2008, http://dx.doi.org/10.1371/journal.pone.0001897

McClellan, Sam, *Integrative Acupressure: A Hands-on Guide to Balancing the Body's Structure and Energy for Health and Healing*, Berkley Publishing Group, 1998.

Nightsong (Observing Member), *What does the Catholic Church say about religious ecstasy?*, November 21st 2007, Catholic Answers Forum, http://forums.catholic.com/showthread.php?t=200184

Notovitch, Nicolas, *The Unknown Life of Jesus Christ*, New York, 1890.

Pradel, Father Andrew, St. Vincent Ferrer-The Angel of the Judgement, Tan Books, 2001.

Saint John of the Cross, *Dark Knight of the Soul*, Riverhead Hardcover, 2002

SparkNotes Editors. "SparkNote on Albert Einstein." SparkNotes LLC 2005
http://www.sparknotes.com/biography/einstein/ (accessed February 19, 2017).

Suttie, Jill, *How Mindfulness Is Changing Law Enforcement*, The Greater Good, May 18th, 2016. http://greatergood.berkeley.edu/article/item/how_mindfulness_is_changing_law_enforcement

Wanshel, Elyse, *Police Officers Get Their Serenity On, Meditate Before Hitting the Streets*, Awesome X Infinity, April 20th 2016, http://www.huffingtonpost.com/entry/canadian-cops-police-officers-meditate-at-temple-training_us_5717c7f0e4b-0479c59d6bd46

Yogananda, Paramahansa, *Autobiography of a Yogi*, Self Realization Fellowship, 1998.

Yogananda, Paramahansa, *The Yoga of Jesus: Understanding the Hidden Teachings of the Gospels*, Self Realization Fellowship, 2007.

Yogananda, Paramahansa, *The Second Coming of Christ: The Resurrection of the Christ Within You 2 Volume Set, Box Edition*, Self Realization Fellowship, 2008.

Zimmerman, F. Benedict, *Teresa of Avila. Interior Castle*, Wilder Publications, 2008.

AN ALTAR BOY GOES EAST:

DISCOVERING THE HEALING JESUS

Ted O'Brien

Made in the USA
Lexington, KY
15 March 2017